Slim Chicken!

115+ Delicious, Healthy Chicken Recipes That Help You Drop Stubborn Pounds without Hunger

Kristina Gonzalez

with the editors of Prevention

This book is intended as a reference volume only, not as a medical manual.
The information given here is designed to help you make informed decisions about your health.
It is not intended as a substitute for any treatment that may have been prescribed by your doctor.
If you suspect that you have a medical problem, we urge you to seek competent medical help.

The information in this book is meant to supplement, not replace, proper exercise training.
All forms of exercise pose some inherent risks. The editors and publisher advise readers to take full responsibility for their safety and know their limits. Before practicing the exercises in this book, be sure that your equipment is well-maintained, and do not take risks beyond your level of experience, aptitude, training, and fitness.
The exercise and dietary programs in this book are not intended as a substitute for any exercise routine or dietary regimen that may have been prescribed by your doctor. As with all exercise and dietary programs, you should get your doctor's approval before beginning.

Mention of specific companies, organizations, or authorities in this book does not imply endorsement by the author or publisher, nor does mention of specific companies, organizations, or authorities imply that they endorse this book, its author, or the publisher.

Internet addresses and phone numbers given in this book were accurate at the time it went to press.

Printed in China

PHOTOGRAPHS BY Mitch Mandel

BOOK DESIGN BY Susan Eugster

Recipes By Julissa Roberts and Jennifer Kushnier

Library of Congress Cataloging-in-Publication Data is on file with the publisher.

ISBN 978-1-63565-314-4

4 6 8 10 9 7 5 paperback

HEARST

Contents

The Whole Bird

Love Your Leftover Chicken

Ground Chicken & Sausage Goodness

The New Weight Loss **Wonder Food**

One of the health industry's best-kept secrets is hiding in plain sight. You can drop pounds and achieve amazing health without eating weird health foods or spiralizing a zucchini in place of spaghetti. All you have to do is prioritize the most underrated protein source around: chicken. Make chicken (or the egg) a part of each of your meals and you really can shrink belly fat without feeling hungry, battling cravings, or doubling your grocery bill.

And don't worry, we're not talking about that broiled chicken breast with steamed veggies that makes dinner about as exciting as watching C-SPAN with your cat (not that there's anything wrong with that). When we worked with our test kitchen to create this guide, our instructions were simple: make it impossible for anyone to get sick of chicken. Well, they delivered. Slim Chicken! serves up Chicken Parm Sliders, Asian-Style Chili Chicken "Nachos," and a Bacon and Egg Ramen Bowl, among more than 115 dishes that will please the pickiest of eaters.

Why We Love Chicken

As it turns out, chicken is even more versatile than Meryl Streep, but that's just one of many powerful reasons to love it. Including chicken (or eggs) with every meal offers the easiest, cheapest, and tastiest way to fill up on fewer calories. When you embrace this lifestyle, you experience many benefits.

YOU'LL NEVER CRAVE SECONDS. When you consume chicken or eggs with every meal, you automatically take in regular doses of protein, which is the most satisfying of the three macronutrients. Women who consumed 30 percent of their calories from protein felt less hungry between meals than did women who consumed half as much protein, but the same number of calories, found a study published in the journal *Obesity*.

YOU'LL DITCH BELLY FAT WITHOUT SHUTTING DOWN YOUR METABOLISM. Perhaps you've heard that your metabolism slows as your body size shrinks, eventually causing you to hit a plateau. But men and women who consumed 30 percent of their calories from protein were able to slim down all over— including their bellies—while also preserving lean body mass (muscle tissue). This, in turn, helped to preserve metabolism.

YOU'LL KEEP DINNER INTERESTING. Thanks to the more than 115 recipes in this guide, you'll learn how to use every single part of the bird. You'll roast it whole with a wide variety of seasonings, and then use leftovers for sandwiches, salads, soups, casseroles, and more. You'll use chicken sausage, too, as well as ground chicken to make easy dishes like Sloppy Joes (page 135) and Asian Chicken Meatballs (page 141).

YOU'LL SPEND HALF AS MUCH AT THE GROCERY STORE. Compared to beef and pork, the retail price of chicken is significantly lower. The National Chicken Council reported in 2016 that beef was $6.20 per pound, pork was $3.78 per pound, and a broiler chicken was $1.42 per pound. Take a look next time you're at the grocery store. Chicken, by far, gives you the best bang for your buck.

YOU'LL NEVER HEAR COMPLAINTS ABOUT WHAT YOU'VE JUST COOKED. You've probably heard someone say, "I don't eat red meat," "I don't care for pork," or "I hate fish." How often do people say these things about chicken? Never, and with the 28-day plan and the 100+ chicken recipes we've packed into this guide, no one will complain of boredom, either.

YOU WON'T NEGLECT YOUR HEALTH IN THE NAME OF WEIGHT LOSS. Chicken is rich in B-vitamins, iron, zinc, selenium, and copper. Compared to other types of meat, chicken also contains a healthier ratio of fats. About a third of chicken fat is saturated, with the rest composed of a blend of good-for-you monounsaturated fats, omega 6 fats and even some of those omega 3s that have a way of always being in the news. This all adds up to important health benefits.

Substituting one daily serving of red meat with chicken can reduce the risk of cardiovascular disease by 19 percent and breast cancer by 24 percent, finds research. This isn't to say that red meat is bad for you. It's only that the nutrients and unique fat profile in chicken trumps that of other types of meat. And when consumed along with fruit, legumes and other healthy foods, chicken helps to prevent the development of type 2 diabetes as well as drive down risk of death in people already diagnosed with it.

YOU'LL FIND COMFORT OUTSIDE OF THE COOKIE JAR. Chicken takes comfort food to a whole new level. Our bodies use tryptophan, an amino acid found in chicken, to create serotonin, which helps you maintain a good mood, feel relaxed, and sleep better. Also, tryptophan intake is associated with a lower a risk of depression, according to a study in the *Journal of Nutrition*.

We've given you all the benefits that Slim Chicks reap from eating chicken. Now it's time to experience the power of chicken for yourself.

The 28-Day Meal Plan

To slim down, you need only do one thing: consume chicken (or eggs) at every meal. That one strategy will help you to get approximately 20 to 30 grams (or more!) of protein at every meal—enough to fill you up, preserve your metabolism, and help you to shed fat. It's a truly simple strategy, but to consume the right amounts—not to mention keep meals interesting – you need a plan. That's where we come in.

On pages 11 to 25, you'll find four weeks worth of chicken meals. Each day adds up to between 1,300 to 1,500 calories. These protein-rich meals will be filling, so eat until you're satisfied, not stuffed. If you feel like you've eaten enough, don't force yourself to eat every bite. Save the leftovers for another meal. You can easily reheat the majority of the recipes as needed (perfect for meal prepping). Also, feel welcome to swap in alternative meals anytime you want.

To reduce meal prep even more, you'll notice that we occasionally suggest roasting a whole chicken and using the leftovers for other recipes. If you're really crunched for time, though, you can buy a pre-cooked rotisserie chicken. Pre-cooked chicken makes for simple meal prep and let's you spend less time in the kitchen during the week.

To make this plan as easy as possible, we've also included grocery lists for each week. You'll use some of these items throughout the whole plan. These household staples—such as olive oil, spices, bread, butter, and more–appear in the pantry list. You'll find recommendations for our favorite products, like Applegate Farms and Ezekiel Bread, but feel free to choose your own favorites. You'll obviously use other items—such as fresh produce and chicken—each week. You'll find those listed throughout the meal plans.

FAQs

We have the answers to every question that you might have before starting the 28-day plan.

What can I drink?

Avoid sugar-sweetened drinks, including fruit juice, as these add unnecessary calories. Instead, stick with beverages that contain no calories. For the most part, that means water, coffee, unsweetened tea, and diet soda. As a general rule, try to drink eight to 12 ounces of water for every two hours you're awake. That ensures that you're well hydrated. Add a squeeze of lemon or try an infused water to add variety. And, of course, zero-calorie, naturally-flavored waters like Hint, Perrier, Lacroix, and Saratoga Spring Water are all great choices.

Can I have wine?

Alcohol offers pros and cons. It contains calories, of course, and can also stimulate your appetite and negatively impact your sleep, which can make it harder for you stay on the plan. On the plus side, it appears to improve levels of good HDL cholesterol and helps take the edge off after a stressful day. Our recommendation: drink it, but in moderation.

Stick to no more than one drink a night. And regardless of how many you consume at one time, limit yourself to four total drinks for any given week while you're on this 28-day plan.

Can I ever eat snacks?

The meal plan includes three meals a day and no snacks. That's because each meal's 20 to 30 grams of protein will help keep you full. However, mental cravings can still be challenge, and eating habits that have been ingrained for many years are hard to break. So we've also provided you with a list of low-calorie but filling snacks on page 26 that you can turn to if you need a holdover until your next meal.

Can I eat out?

Absolutely, just follow these rules. Choose items that are around 500 calories and contain a protein-rich food such as chicken (obviously), turkey, beef, or fish. If the calories aren't listed, choose a chicken dish with vegetables. Keep in mind that most restaurant dishes are oversized, many containing more than a thousand calories. When in doubt, ask for a box right away so you can take half the dish home for another meal.

We hope we've just answered all of your questions. Now it's time to dig in. The 28 day plan contains recipes that are so diverse that you'll forget that you're eating chicken for every meal. At the end of these four weeks you'll be the master of all things chicken.

HOUSEHOLD STAPLES

BROTHS

- ☐ Low-sodium chicken broth (32-ounce container)
- ☐ Low-sodium vegetable broth (32-ounce container)

BAKING NEEDS

- ☐ All purpose flour (5 pound bag)
- ☐ Corn starch (16-ounce package)
- ☐ Panko breadcrumbs (8-ounce can)
- ☐ Vanilla extract (2-ounce bottle)

BREADS

- ☐ Whole-wheat spaghetti (1 pound)
- ☐ Whole-wheat pitas (6-count package)
- ☐ Whole-grain bread, such as Ezekiel
- ☐ Whole-wheat tortillas (8" diameter)

CANNED GOODS

- ☐ Black beans (15-ounce can)
- ☐ Chickpeas (15-ounce can)
- ☐ Pinto beans (15-ounce can)
- ☐ White beans (15-ounce can)

GRAINS

- ☐ White rice (5 pound bag)
- ☐ Brown Rice (5 pound bag)
- ☐ Brown Lentils (1 pound bag)
- ☐ Basmati Rice (32-ounce bag)
- ☐ Instant Grits (24-ounce can)
- ☐ Orzo (16-ounce box)
- ☐ Quinoa (12-ounce bag)

NUTS

- ☐ Nut butter, peanut and almond (16-ounce jar)
- ☐ Unsalted Whole Almonds (14-ounce bag)
- ☐ Unsalted shelled pistachios (6-ounce bag)
- ☐ Pepitas (pumpkin seeds), hulled (one 4-ounce package)
- ☐ Pecans (2.25-ounce bag)

OILS AND VINEGARS

- ☐ Olive Oil
- ☐ Canola oil
- ☐ Sesame oil
- ☐ Sherry vinegar
- ☐ Apple cider vinegar
- ☐ Balsamic vinegar
- ☐ Low-sodium Soy sauce

PRODUCE

- ☐ Garlic (1 or 2 heads)
- ☐ Ginger root (¼ pound)
- ☐ Red potatoes (3 pounds)
- ☐ Shallots (1 pound)
- ☐ Sweet potatoes (1 pound)
- ☐ Yellow onions (1 pound)

REFRIGERATED FOODS

- ☐ Breakfast chicken sausage, such as Applegate Farms (7-ounce box)
- ☐ Grated Parmigiano-Reggiano (5-ounce tub)
- ☐ Feta cheese (6-ounce package)
- ☐ Shredded cheddar cheese (8-ounce bag)
- ☐ Sour cream (8-ounce tub)
- ☐ Butter (1 pound box)
- ☐ Mayonnaise (30-ounce jar)

SPICES

- ☐ Kosher Salt
- ☐ Black pepper
- ☐ Cumin
- ☐ Cinnamon sticks
- ☐ Crush red pepper flakes
- ☐ Cinnamon
- ☐ Chili powder
- ☐ Garlic powder
- ☐ 1 jar Garam Masala spice blend, such as McCormick
- ☐ Smoked Paprika
- ☐ Yellow curry powder

SAUCES AND CONDIMENTS

- ☐ Hoisin sauce (8.5-ounce jar)
- ☐ Molasses (12-ounce jar)
- ☐ Prepared horseradish (6-ounce jar)
- ☐ Tikka masala sauce (15-ounces jar), such as Pataks's, found in the ethnic food aisle
- ☐ Salsa (15.5-ounce jar)
- ☐ Sriracha
- ☐ Dijon Mustard
- ☐ Dill Pickles (24-ounce jar)

SWEETENERS

- ☐ Dark brown sugar (32-ounce bag)
- ☐ White sugar (4 pound bag)

WEEK 1

Grocery List

PROTEIN

- ☐ 2 whole chickens (3 to 4 pounds each) OR 1 whole chicken (3 to 4 pounds) and 1 rotisserie chicken (if you don't plan on making The Ultimate Roasted Chicken)
- ☐ 8 ounces boneless skinless chicken breast
- ☐ 4 (2 pounds) bone-in, skin-on chicken thighs
- ☐ 4 (1¾ pounds) chicken drumsticks
- ☐ ¾ pound ground chicken
- ☐ ¼ pound sliced deli chicken breast
- ☐ 1 package (4 ounces) smoked salmon
- ☐ ½ dozen eggs

BREAD

- ☐ 1 pumpernickel bagel

DAIRY

- ☐ 1 tub (32 ounces) plain low-fat yogurt

PRODUCE

- ☐ 1 avocado
- ☐ 4 to 6 baby bok choy
- ☐ 1 small head broccoli
- ☐ 1 pound Brussels sprouts
- ☐ 1 medium head cauliflower
- ☐ 1 ½ pound carrots
- ☐ 6 medium shiitake mushroom caps
- ☐ 1 package (12 ounces) snap peas
- ☐ 2 medium zucchini or summer squash
- ☐ 1 package (16 ounces) baby spinach
- ☐ 1 bag (14 ounces) shredded cabbage
- ☐ 1 or 2 Fresno chiles
- ☐ 1 small bunch fresh basil leaves
- ☐ 1 small bunch cilantro
- ☐ 1 ounce fresh dill
- ☐ 1 bunch scallions
- ☐ 2 lemons
- ☐ 1 lime
- ☐ 2 small/medium red onions
- ☐ 1 container (16 ounces) strawberries

PACKAGED FOODS

- ☐ 1 can (28 ounces) crushed tomatoes
- ☐ 1 jar (12 ounces) roasted red peppers
- ☐ 1 jar (16 ounces) salsa verde
- ☐ 1 tub (10 ounces) plain hummus
- ☐ 1 bag of oven baked tortilla chips, such as Tostitos Baked (save leftover for week 2)
- ☐ 1 bag (14.4 ounces) frozen corn kernels (save leftovers for week 2)

MENUS

MONDAY

BREAKFAST

Simple Scramble

2 large eggs scrambled with 2 tablespoons shredded cheddar cheese
3 chicken sausage links
1 slice whole-wheat toast
½ cup sliced strawberries
(416 CALORIES/29 GRAMS PROTEIN)

LUNCH

Chicken and Roasted Red Pepper Wrap

2 tablespoons plain hummus
1 whole-wheat tortilla
4 ounces deli chicken breast
2 tablespoons chopped roasted red pepper
2 tablespoons crumbled feta
Enjoy with 1 sliced apple and 1 tablespoon of almond butter.
(479 CALORIES / 34 GRAMS PROTEIN)

DINNER

The Ultimate Roasted Whole Chicken (page 81) **with the seasoning of your choice**

1 cup broccoli florets cooked with 1 teaspoon of olive and 1 clove of garlic, minced
(558 CALORIES/45 GRAMS PROTEIN)

TUESDAY

BREAKFAST

Huevos Rancheros Jars (page 35)

(424 CALORIES/18 GRAMS PROTEIN)
Save the second jar for breakfast tomorrow!

LUNCH

Chicken and Roasted Red Pepper Wrap

2 tablespoons plain hummus
1 whole-wheat tortilla
4 ounces deli chicken breast
2 tablespoons chopped roasted red pepper
2 tablespoons crumbled feta
Enjoy with 1 sliced apple and 1 tablespoon of almond butter.
(479 CALORIES / 34 GRAMS PROTEIN)

DINNER

Thai Peanut Noodles with Chicken and Scallions (page 100)

(517 CALORIES/37 GRAMS PROTEIN)

WEDNESDAY

BREAKFAST

Leftover Huevos Rancheros Jars

(424 CALORIES/18 GRAMS PROTEIN)

LUNCH

Leftover Thai Peanut Noodles with Chicken and Scallions

(517 CALORIES/37 GRAMS PROTEIN)

DINNER

Dumpling Stir Fry (page 128)

(547 CALORIES/37 GRAMS PROTEIN)

THURSDAY

BREAKFAST

Not Yo' Momma's Toad in a Hole (page 33)

(358 CALORIES/30 GRAMS PROTEIN)

Use half the bagel and reserve the remaining salmon mixture for tomorrow's breakfast.

LUNCH

Leftover Dumpling Stir-Fry

(547 CALORIES/37 GRAMS PROTEIN)

DINNER

One Pan Chicken Tikka Dinner (page 75)

(472 CALORIES/46 GRAMS PROTEIN)

FRIDAY

BREAKFAST

Leftover Not Yo Momma's Toad in a Hole

(358 CALORIES/30 GRAMS PROTEIN)

LUNCH

Zucchini Noodles with Pesto, Chicken, and Chickpeas (page 101)

(532 CALORIES/40 GRAMS PROTEIN)

DINNER

Leftover One Pan Chicken Tikka Dinner

(472 CALORIES/46 GRAMS PROTEIN)

SATURDAY

BREAKFAST

Simple Scramble:

2 large eggs scrambled with 2 tablespoons shredded cheddar cheese
3 chicken sausage links
1 slice whole-wheat toast
½ cup sliced strawberries

(416 CALORIES/29 GRAMS PROTEIN)

LUNCH

Leftover Zucchini Noodles with Pesto, Chicken, and Chickpeas

(532 CALORIES/40 GRAMS PROTEIN)

DINNER

Slow Cooker BBQ Pulled Chicken Flat Breads (page 57)

(447 CALORIES/33 GRAMS PROTEIN)

SUNDAY

BREAKFAST

Eggs with Grits and Mushrooms (page 33)

(393 CALORIES/19 GRAMS PROTEIN)

LUNCH

Leftover Slow Cooker BBQ Pulled Chicken Flat Breads

(447 CALORIES/33 GRAMS PROTEIN)

DINNER

Roasted Dry-Brine Chicken and Vegetables (page 88)

(426 CALORIES/33 GRAMS PROTEIN)

WEEK 2

Grocery List

PROTEIN

- ☐ I whole chicken (3 to 4 pounds each) OR I rotisserie chicken (if you don't plan on making The Ultimate Roasted Chicken)
- ☐ 2 boneless skinless chicken breast (6 ounces to 8 ounces each)
- ☐ 4 boneless skinless chicken thighs (2 pounds)
- ☐ Raw spicy chicken sausage (4 ounces), found in the poultry section
- ☐ hot Italian chicken sausage (8 ounces)
- ☐ I pound ground chicken
- ☐ I dozen eggs

DAIRY

- ☐ I container (I5 ounces) part-skim ricotta cheese
- ☐ I container (5.3 ounces) low fat plain Greek yogurt

PRODUCE

- ☐ 2 avocados
- ☐ I small butternut squash OR I package (I6 ounces) frozen butternut squash
- ☐ I small head broccoli
- ☐ I pint cherry tomatoes
- ☐ 2 limes
- ☐ I large bunch of scallions
- ☐ I bag (5 ounces) arugula
- ☐ I package (I6 ounces) baby spinach
- ☐ I small bunch basil
- ☐ I bunch cilantro
- ☐ I small bunch mint
- ☐ I package (4.4 ounces) blueberries
- ☐ I container (I6 ounces) strawberries
- ☐ I red bell pepper
- ☐ I green bell pepper
- ☐ 2 jalapeñoes

PACKAGED FOODS

- ☐ I jar (I6 ounce) artichoke hearts
- ☐ I jar (I5 ounces) Kimchi, found in the refrigerated produce section
- ☐ I jar (I4 ounces) peppadew peppers
- ☐ I can tomato paste (6 ounce)
- ☐ I can (I4 ounces) unsalted crushed tomatoes
- ☐ I jar (I6 ounces) salsa verde
- ☐ I bottle (I-ounce) sesame seeds, such as McCormick
- ☐ I package nori sheets, such as Sea's Gift, found in the ethnic food aisle

MENU

MONDAY

BREAKFAST

Simple Scramble

2 large eggs scrambled with 2 tablespoons shredded cheddar cheese
3 chicken sausage links
1 slice whole-wheat toast
½ cup sliced strawberries
(416 CALORIES/29 GRAMS PROTEIN)

LUNCH

Leftover Roasted Dry-Brine Chicken and Vegetables

(426 CALORIES/33 GRAMS PROTEIN)

DINNER

Eggs in Purgatory (page 30)

(518 CALORIES/32 GRAMS PROTEIN)

Don't put all those eggs in! Save the tomato mixture for tomorrow's brunch and add the extra 2 eggs in for a hearty morning meal.

TUESDAY

BREAKFAST

Leftover Eggs in Purgatory

(518 CALORIES/32 GRAMS PROTEIN)

LUNCH

Quick Chicken Salad

Mix together:
2 cups baby spinach
¼ cup cherry tomatoes
¼ cup garbanzo beans, canned
4 ounces cooked chicken breast
2 tablespoons crumbled feta cheese
2 tablespoons balsamic vinaigrette
(406 CALORIES/42 GRAMS PROTEIN)

DINNER

Loaded Taco Bowls (page 131)

(472 CALORIES/31 GRAMS PROTEIN)

This recipe makes 4 hearty servings, perfect for lunch for the week!

WEDNESDAY

BREAKFAST

Easy Avocado Toast with Eggs

Mash ½ of an avocado on slice of whole-grain toast. Top with 2 eggs, cooked your favorite way. Season with salt and pepper to taste.

(372 CALORIES/18 GRAMS PROTEIN)

LUNCH

Leftover Loaded Taco Bowl

(472 CALORIES/31 GRAMS PROTEIN)

DINNER

Curry Mint Chicken with Butternut Squash (page 48)

(453 CALORIES/42 GRAMS PROTEIN)

THURSDAY

BREAKFAST

Huevos Rancheros Jars (page 35)

(424 CALORIES/18 GRAMS PROTEIN)

Save the second jar for breakfast tomorrow.

LUNCH

Leftover Loaded Taco Bowl

(472 calories/31 grams protein)

DINNER

Leftover Curry Mint Chicken with Butternut Squash

(453 CALORIES/42 GRAMS PROTEIN)

FRIDAY

BREAKFAST

Leftover Huevos Ranchero Jar

(424 CALORIES/18 GRAMS PROTEIN)

LUNCH

Leftover Loaded Taco Bowl

(472 CALORIES/31 GRAMS PROTEIN)

DINNER

Spicy Sauteed Chicken with Kimchi (page 68)

Serve with 2 cups baby spinach mixed with ¼ cup cherry tomatoes, ¼ sliced cucumber, and 2 tablespoons balsamic vinaigrette dressing.

(520 CALORIES/37 GRAMS PROTEIN)

SATURDAY

BREAKFAST

Easy Avocado Toast with Eggs

Mash ½ of an avocado on slice of whole-grain toast. Top with 2 eggs, cooked your favorite way. Season with salt and pepper to taste.

(372 CALORIES/18 GRAMS PROTEIN)

LUNCH

Leftover Spicy Sauteed Chicken with Kimchi

(400 CALORIES/35 GRAMS PROTEIN)

DINNER

Orzo Diavolo with Sausage and 'Chokes (page 127)

(589 CALORIES/30 GRAMS PROTEIN)

SUNDAY

BREAKFAST

Sweet Berry Omelets (page 39)

(350 CALORIES/22 GRAMS PROTEIN)

When you make the eggs for this recipe, only make half the recommended amount. Save half the berry mixture, and make fresh eggs for tomorrow's breakfast.

LUNCH

Leftover Orzo Diavolo with Sausage and 'Chokes

(589 CALORIES/30 GRAMS PROTEIN)

DINNER

The Ultimate Roasted Whole Chicken (page 81) with the seasoning of your choice

Serve with 1 cup broccoli florets cooked with 1 teaspoon of olive and 1 clove of garlic, minced

(558 CALORIES/45 GRAMS PROTEIN)

WEEK 3

Grocery List

PROTEIN

- ☐ 1 whole chicken (3 to 4 pounds each) OR 1 rotisserie chicken (if you don't plan on making The Ultimate Roasted Chicken)
- ☐ 2 boneless, skinless chicken thighs
- ☐ ½ pound chicken tenders
- ☐ ¼ pound deli chicken breast
- ☐ 1 package (16 ounces) bacon
- ☐ 1 package (4 ounces) prosciutto
- ☐ 2 dozen eggs
- ☐ 1 package (8 ounces) fresh mozzarella
- ☐ 1 bag (8 ounces) shredded mozzarella cheese
- ☐ ½ gallon 2% milk

PRODUCE

- ☐ 2 avocados
- ☐ 1 pound asparagus
- ☐ 2 pounds broccoli crowns
- ☐ ½ pound Brussels sprouts
- ☐ 1 small bunch scallions
- ☐ 1 pint cherry tomatoes
- ☐ ½ pound cremini or button mushrooms
- ☐ 6 medium shiitake mushroom caps
- ☐ 1 ½ ounces fresh watercress
- ☐ 1 package (16 ounces) baby spinach
- ☐ 1 small head romaine (5 to 6 ounces)
- ☐ 2 red bell peppers
- ☐ 1 package (.75 ounces) fresh chives
- ☐ 1 package (.75 ounces) fresh sage
- ☐ 1 lemon
- ☐ 1 small orange
- ☐ 1 medium apple, such as red delicious or gala
- ☐ 1 container (16 ounces) strawberries

PACKAGED FOODS

- ☐ 1 tub (17.6 ounces) miso paste, in the oriental or refrigerated section
- ☐ 1 jar (8-ounces) prepared pesto
- ☐ 1 jar (7.5 ounces) sun dried tomatoes
- ☐ 1 can (8 ounces) tomato sauce (not pasta sauce)
- ☐ 1 jar (12 ounces) orange marmalade
- ☐ 1 jar (16 ounces) tahini, found in the peanut butter section
- ☐ 1 bag (16 ounces) frozen green peas (save remaining for week 4)

DAIRY

- ☐ 1 bag (8 ounces) shredded cheese such as Cheddar, Swiss or horseradish, divided

MENU

BREAKFAST

Leftover Sweet Berry Omelet

(350 CALORIES/22 GRAMS PROTEIN)

LUNCH

Quick Chicken Salad

Mix together:
2 cups baby spinach
¼ cup cherry tomatoes
¼ cup garbanzo beans, canned
4 ounces cooked chicken breast
2 tablespoons crumbled feta cheese
2 tablespoons balsamic vinaigrette
(406 CALORIES/42 GRAMS PROTEIN)

DINNER

Green Envy Rice Bowl (page 112)

(552 CALORIES/32 GRAMS PROTEIN)

This makes 4 servings, perfect for lunch for the rest of the week! Leftover chicken from Sunday night comes handy for this recipe. Remember, slice your avocado as needed so it doesn't get brown.

BREAKFAST

Simple Scramble:

2 large eggs scrambled with 2 tablespoons shredded cheddar cheese
3 chicken sausage links
1 slice whole-wheat toast
½ cup sliced strawberries
(416 CALORIES/29 GRAMS PROTEIN)

LUNCH

Leftover Green Envy Rice Bowl

(552 CALORIES/32 GRAMS PROTEIN)

DINNER

Chicken Sausage and Apple Power Salad (page 122)

½ medium baked sweet potato with 1 teaspoon of butter
(482 CALORIES/21 GRAMS PROTEIN)

WEDNESDAY

BREAKFAST

Cheese and Egg Quesadilla (page 43)

(474 CALORIES/24 GRAMS PROTEIN)

This makes 2 servings, so save the rest for tomorrow's breakfast.

LUNCH

Leftover Green Envy Rice Bowl

(552 CALORIES/32 GRAMS PROTEIN)

DINNER

Leftover Chicken Sausage and Apple Power Salad

½ medium baked sweet potato with 1 teaspoon of butter

(482 CALORIES/21 GRAMS PROTEIN)

THURSDAY

BREAKFAST

Leftover Cheese and Egg Quesadilla

(474 CALORIES/24 GRAMS PROTEIN)

LUNCH

Leftover Green Envy Rice Bowl

(552 CALORIES/32 GRAMS PROTEIN)

DINNER

Orange Chicken and Broccoli Stir-Fry (page 50)

(540 CALORIES/36 GRAMS PROTEIN)

FRIDAY

BREAKFAST

Simple Scramble

2 large eggs scrambled with 2 tablespoons shredded cheddar cheese

3 chicken sausage links

1 slice whole-wheat toast

½ cup sliced strawberries

(416 CALORIES/29 GRAMS PROTEIN)

LUNCH

Leftover Orange Chicken and Broccoli

(540 CALORIES/36 GRAMS PROTEIN)

DINNER

Chicken Thigh Saltimboca (page 78)

1 cup red potatoes roasted in the oven with 1 teaspoon olive oil, and salt and pepper to taste.

(456 CALORIES/29 GRAMS PROTEIN)

SATURDAY

BREAKFAST

Eggs with Grits and Mushrooms (page 33)

(393 CALORIES/19 GRAMS PROTEIN)

LUNCH

Leftover Chicken Thigh Saltimbocca with red potatoes

(456 CALORIES/29 GRAMS PROTEIN)

DINNER

The Ultimate Roasted Whole Chicken (page 81) **with the seasoning of your choice**

Serve with 1 cup broccoli florets cooked with 1 teaspoon of olive and 1 clove of garlic, minced.

(558 CALORIES/45 GRAMS PROTEIN)

SUNDAY

BREAKFAST

Pesto Frittata Muffins (page 40)

(310 CALORIES/20 GRAMS PROTEIN)

This recipe makes 4 servings of muffins, perfect for breakfast for the beginning of the week!

LUNCH

Chicken and Roasted Red Pepper Wrap

2 tablespoons plain hummus
1 whole-wheat tortilla
4 ounces deli chicken breast
2 tablespoons chopped roasted red pepper
2 tablespoons crumbled feta
Enjoy with 1 sliced apple and 1 tablespoon of almond butter.

(479 CALORIES / 34 GRAMS PROTEIN)

DINNER

Arroz con Pollo (page 102)

(516 calories/52 grams protein)

WEEK 4

Grocery List

PROTEIN

☐ 4 boneless skinless chicken breasts (6 ounces to 8 ounces each)

☐ 1 pound chicken tenders

☐ 1 pound ground chicken

☐ ¼ pound sliced deli chicken

☐ 1 dozen eggs

PRODUCE

☐ 1 avocado

☐ 1 small head of broccoli

☐ 1 pint cherry tomatoes

☐ 1 pint grape tomatoes

☐ 1 package (5 ounces) arugula

☐ 1 small head of Boston lettuce

☐ 1 bunch watercress

☐ 1 red bell pepper

☐ 1 yellow bell pepper, diced

☐ 2 jalapeño peppers

☐ 1 small bunch cilantro

☐ 1 small bunch fresh mint

☐ 1 package (.75 ounces) fresh rosemary

☐ 1 package (.75 ounces) fresh thyme

☐ 1 red onion

☐ 1 small bunch scallions

☐ 5 lemons

☐ 1 medium apple, such as red delicious or gala

☐ 1 container (16 ounces) strawberries

PACKAGED FOODS

☐ 1 can (6 ounces) salmon

☐ 1 jar (6 ounces) kalamata olives

☐ 1 can (4 ounces) chopped green chile peppers

☐ 1 can (13.6 ounces) unsweetened coconut milk

MENU

MONDAY

BREAKFAST

Leftover Pesto Frittata Muffins

(310 CALORIES/20 GRAMS PROTEIN)

LUNCH

Leftover Arroz con Pollo

(516 CALORIES/52 GRAMS PROTEIN)

DINNER

Salmon Kedgeree (page 39)

(538 CALORIES/35 GRAMS PROTEIN)

TUESDAY

BREAKFAST

Leftover Pesto Frittata Muffins

(310 CALORIES/20 GRAMS PROTEIN)

LUNCH

Leftover Salmon Kedgeree

(538 CALORIES/35 GRAMS PROTEIN)

DINNER

Chicken Lettuce Tacos with Pickled Strawberry Salsa (page 137)

(431 CALORIES/28 GRAMS PROTEIN)

WEDNESDAY

BREAKFAST

Leftover Pesto Frittata Muffins

(310 CALORIES/20 GRAMS PROTEIN)

LUNCH

Leftover Chicken Lettuce Tacos with Pickled Strawberry Salsa

(431 CALORIES/28 GRAMS PROTEIN)

DINNER

Poached Chicken with White Bean and Watercress Salad (page 48)

(431 CALORIES/45 GRAMS PROTEIN)

THURSDAY

BREAKFAST

Southwest Breakfast Burritos (page 41)

(460 CALORIES/26 GRAMS PROTEIN)

Follow the freezing and reheating instructions for this breakfast burrito so you can have an easy breakfast all week.

LUNCH

Leftover Chicken Lettuce Tacos with Pickled Strawberry Salsa

(431 CALORIES/28 GRAMS PROTEIN)

DINNER

Leftover Chicken with White Bean and Watercress Salad

(431 CALORIES/45 GRAMS PROTEIN)

FRIDAY

BREAKFAST

Leftover Southwest Breakfast Burritos

(460 CALORIES/26 GRAMS PROTEIN)

LUNCH

Leftover Chicken Lettuce Tacos with Pickled Strawberry Salsa

(431 CALORIES/28 GRAMS PROTEIN)

DINNER

Herb-Pounded Chicken with Arugula (page 47)

Serve with 1 cup red potatoes roasted in the oven with olive oil, and salt and pepper to taste

(581 CALORIES/41 GRAMS PROTEIN)

BREAKFAST

Leftover Southwest Breakfast Burritos

(460 CALORIES/26 GRAMS PROTEIN)

LUNCH

Leftover Herb-Pounded Chicken with Arugula

Serve with 1 cup red potatoes roasted in the oven with olive oil, and salt and pepper to taste

(581 CALORIES/41 GRAMS PROTEIN)

DINNER

Oven Baked Chicken Fingers (page 61)

Serve with 1 cup red potatoes roasted in the oven with olive oil, and salt and pepper to taste

Broccoli cooked with 1 teaspoon of olive and 1 clove of garlic, minced

(467 CALORIES/34 GRAMS PROTEIN)

BREAKFAST

Leftover Southwest Breakfast Burritos

(460 CALORIES/26 GRAMS PROTEIN)

LUNCH

Quick Chicken Salad

Mix together:

2 cups baby spinach

¼ cup cherry tomatoes

¼ cup garbanzo beans, canned

4 ounces cooked chicken breast

2 tablespoons crumbled feta cheese

2 tablespoons balsamic vinaigrette

(406 CALORIES/42 GRAMS PROTEIN)

DINNER

Leftover Oven Baked Chicken Fingers

Serve with 1 cup red potatoes roasted in the oven with olive oil, and salt and pepper to taste

Broccoli cooked with 1 teaspoon of olive and 1 clove of garlic, minced

(467 CALORIES/34 GRAMS PROTEIN)

SLIM CHICKEN APPROVED SNACKS

These quick and nutritious snacks will help keep you satisfied between meals. All have a healthy dose of protein. While they're not always as tempting as junk foods, you'll find that if you stick to these types of snacks, they can help you stay on track.

Chicken, Swiss, and Hummus Wraps

Lay a slice of Swiss cheese on a cutting board and top it with 3 slices of deli chicken and 1 tablespoon of hummus. Roll it up (or just fold it in half) and eat.

(155 CALORIES/17 GRAMS PROTEIN)

Spicy Tuna and Crackers

Eat 2.6 ounces of tuna (1 packet, or about 1 can) mixed with a generous helping of salsa (to taste), along with 1 serving (1 ounce, per label) of Triscuits.

(200 CALORIES/21 GRAMS PROTEIN)

Mozzarella Cheese and Apple Slices

Eat 1 ounce of mozzarella with 1 medium apple.

(200 CALORIES/7 GRAMS PROTEIN)

Peanut Butter on Toast

Eat 1 tablespoon of peanut butter on 1 slice of whole-wheat toast.

(165 CALORIES/8 GRAMS PROTEIN)

Asiago Cheese and Pear Slices

Eat 1 ounce of cheese (about 1 slice) with 1 medium pear.

(200 CALORIES/7 GRAMS PROTEIN)

Nuts and Fruit

Eat 1 serving (about 1 tablespoon) of your favorite nut—for instance, almonds, peanuts, pistachios—or pumpkin or sunflower seeds, along with ½ a large piece of fruit or half cup of fruit. (These nutrition facts are based on almonds and a half a large apple, but they're in the ballpark for just about any alternative.)

(228 CALORIES/6 GRAMS PROTEIN)

Yogurt with Fruit

Enjoy 7 ounces of plain yogurt (such as Fage 2%) with 1 cup of sliced strawberries.

(199 CALORIES/21 GRAMS PROTEIN)

Slim Smoothie

Blend 1 scoop vanilla protein powder, 1 cup whole strawberries (fresh or frozen), ½ cup blueberries (fresh or frozen), and 1 cup 2% milk until smooth.

(326 CALORIES/33 GRAMS PROTEIN)

Edamame

Boil or steam (or even microwave) these in-shell and sprinkle them with sea salt or any other seasoning of your choice.

(100 CALORIES/10 GRAMS PROTEIN)

Pistachios

Enjoy ¼ cup shelled pistachios.

(173 CALORIES/6 GRAMS PROTEIN)

Crunchy Veggies and Hummus

Enjoy a fresh vegetable of your choice, like baby carrots or celery, with 2 tablespoons of hummus.

(105 CALORIES/4 GRAMS PROTEIN).

Slim for Life

Now that you've completed the 28-day plan, you may want to continue using the recipes and guidelines. These rules are simple to follow.

RULE #1

Aim for 20-30 grams of protein at each meal.

RULE #2

Monitor your calorie intake, consuming only about 1,300-1,500 calories a day.

RULE #3

Never get bored. Along with what you've just tried in the past four weeks, you've also got 115+ recipes to sample. You can also create your own satisfying meals that are both low-calorie and delicious. As long as you always have chicken in your fridge, you'll never have a reason to stop following this plan.

Tell us about your results by posting to social media using the hashtag #slimchicken. We can't wait to hear from you.

What Came First...

EGGS

Bacon and Eggs Ramen Bowl

PREP TIME: 5 minutes **TOTAL TIME:** 20 minutes Serves 2

2 slices turkey bacon

2 scallions, thinly sliced, whites and greens kept separate

4 slices ginger

2 cloves garlic, minced

4 cups low sodium chicken broth

1 tablespoon low sodium soy sauce

1 package (3 ounces) ramen noodle, seasoning packet discarded

2 cups small broccoli florets

1 cup baby power greens mix or baby spinach

2 eggs

½ tsp sesame oil

Sriracha or hot sauce, if desired

1. In a 2-quart saucepan over medium heat cook the bacon until crisp, about 4 minutes. Remove from the pan and add the scallion whites, ginger, and garlic, stirring until fragrant, about 1 minute.

2. Stir in the broth and soy sauce and bring to a boil. Add the ramen noodles, broccoli, and baby greens, cook until the noodles are tender, about 3 minutes. Reduce the heat to a simmer, using a slotted spoon, divide all the solids among 2 bowls. Carefully crack the eggs into the simmering broth, keeping them separate. Cook until the whites are set but the yolk is still runny, about 2 minutes.

3. Place the poached eggs on top of the noodles in the bowls. Pour the broth into the bowl and crumble in the bacon. Top with the scallion greens, sesame oil, and a hearty squirt of Sriracha, if desired.

NUTRITION (PER SERVING):

322 calories, **23 g protein**, 39 g carbohydrates, 6 g fiber, 2 g sugars, 8 g fat, 2 g saturated fat, 939 mg sodium

Bacon and Eggs Ramen Bowl

Eggs in Purgatory (Shakshuka)

PREP TIME: 5 minutes **TOTAL TIME:** 15 minutes Serves 2

1 tablespoon canola oil

3 cloves garlic, minced

1 link (4 ounces) raw spicy chicken sausage, casing removed

1 green bell pepper, chopped

1 can (14 ounces) unsalted crushed tomatoes

1 teaspoon hot paprika

Kosher salt and ground black pepper

4 eggs

2 whole wheat pitas

In a medium skillet, heat the oil over medium heat. Add the garlic and cook until fragrant, about 1 minute. Add the sausage and bell pepper and stir, breaking up the sausage, until browned, about 4 minutes. Add the tomatoes, paprika and a pinch of salt and pepper. Bring to a simmer. Using a spoon make 4 holes in the sauce and carefully crack the 1 egg into each hole. Cover the skillet and cook until the whites set and the yolks are still runny, about 3 minutes. Serve with the pita.

NUTRITION (PER SERVING):
518 calories, **32 g protein**, 47 g carbohydrates, 10 g fiber, 9 g sugars, 23 g fat, 5 g saturated fat, 943 mg sodium

Eggs in Purgatory
(Shakshuka)

Gallo Pinto con Huevo (Costa Rican Fried Egg over Black Beans and Rice)

PREP TIME: 5 minutes **TOTAL TIME:** 20 minutes Serves 2

1 tablespoon canola oil

½ cup chopped onion

½ cup chopped red bell pepper

1 clove garlic, chopped

Pinch of kosher salt

¼ cup dry white wine

½ teaspoon ground cumin

¼ cup canned tomato sauce

1 can (15 ounces) low-sodium black beans, drained and rinsed

1 cup water

1 ½ cups cooked brown rice

1 tablespoon Salsa Lizano or Worcestershire sauce + more to taste

4 eggs

Sprinkle of cilantro

In a 4-quart pot over medium, heat the canola oil, onion, bell pepper, garlic , and a pinch of salt and cook until the onion is translucent, about 5 minutes. Add the wine and boil until almost dry, about 2 minutes. Add the cumin and tomato sauce and simmer. Add the beans and water, bring to a boil, and cook until the beans and water are the same level, about 5 minutes. Add the rice and stir to heat through and combine. Stir in the Salsa Lizano or Worcestershire sauce, adding more to taste. In a large nonstick skillet, fry the eggs to your liking. Divide the rice and beans between 2 plates, top with the eggs and sprinkle with cilantro.

Note: Salsa Lizano is found in nearly every Costa Rican home, restaurant, and roadside food stand. Smooth, light brown and vegetable-based, this sauce has a touch of sweetness and a hearty punch of spice, including cumin, mustard, and turmeric. It's most commonly served as a condiment, but it's also used as a marinade for beef, pork, and chicken. You can find it online or at your local Latin market.

NUTRITION (PER SERVING):

550 calories, **26 g protein**, 65 g carbohydrates, 14 g fiber, 7 g sugar, 18 g fat, 4 g saturated fat, 689 mg sodium

Not Yo Momma's Toad in a Hole

PREP TIME: 5 minutes **TOTAL TIME:** 15 minutes Serves 2

1 pumpernickel bagel

2 eggs

1 tablespoon water

2 ounces chopped smoked salmon

1 tablespoon chopped fresh dill

½ teaspoon prepared horseradish

2 tablespoons sour cream

Halve the bagel and enlarge the hole in the middle to about 2 inches. Place cut sides down in nonstick skillet over medium heat, crack an egg in the middle of each bagel slice, cover and cook 4 minutes. Lift the lid, sprinkle the water around the bagels, cover and cook 2 minutes more. Meanwhile, mix the smoked salmon, dill, horseradish, and sour cream and set aside. Serve with salmon salad on the side.

NUTRITION (PER SERVING):

358 calories, **30 g protein**, 34 g carbohydrates, 3 g fiber, 6 g sugar, 12 g fat, 4 g saturated fat, 411 mg sodium

Eggs with Grits and Mushrooms

PREP TIME: 5 minutes **TOTAL TIME:** 15 minutes Serves 1

½ cup instant grits

6 medium shiitake mushroom caps, sliced

½ clove garlic, minced

½ cup low-sodium vegetable broth

2 eggs

Kosher salt and ground black pepper

1. Cook the grits according to package directions. In a medium nonstick skillet over medium-high heat, cook the mushrooms and garlic in the broth, stirring occasionally, until most of the liquid absorbs, about 5 minutes. Stir into the grits and wipe out the skillet.

2 .Coat the skillet with cooking spray and return the skillet to medium heat. Fry the eggs sunny-side up until the whites are set and the yolk is done to your liking, 2 to 3 minutes.

3. Transfer the grits to a bowl and top with the eggs. Sprinkle with a pinch of salt and black pepper.

NUTRITION (PER SERVING):

393 calories, **19 g protein**, 52 g carbohydrates, 5 g fiber, 4 g sugar, 12 g fat, 3 g saturated fat, 896 mg sodium

Bacon, Egg, and Asparagus Brunch Salad

PREP TIME: 10 minutes **TOTAL TIME:** 40 minutes Serves 2

4 slices turkey bacon, diced

3 tablespoons olive oil

1 large shallot, minced

¼ cup sherry vinegar

2 tablespoons chopped parsley leaves

1 tablespoon chopped thyme leaves

2 teaspoons Dijon mustard

½ teaspoon ground black pepper

½ pound asparagus, trimmed

2 large eggs

5 to 6 ounces baby arugula leaves (about 6 cups)

1. Add the bacon to a large skillet and cook over medium high heat until crisp, about 8 minutes. Transfer to a paper towel lined plate with a slotted spoon.

2. Reduce the heat to medium, and the oil and shallots; cook until tender, about 4 minutes. Add the vinegar, scraping up the browned bits with a wooden spoon. Remove from heat and stir in herbs, mustard, and pepper; set the dressing aside.

3. Bring a medium saucepan of water to a simmer over medium high heat. Reduce the heat to low, add the asparagus and cook until crisp tender, about 2 minutes. Remove from the water and set aside.

4. Return the water to a low simmer, swirl the water, and drop one egg into the middle. Cook the egg until the white is set but the yolk is runny, about 4 minutes. Remove with a slotted spoon and transfer to a plate. Repeat with the remaining eggs.

5. Toss the salad greens with 2 tablespoons of the dressing; divide the salad greens among 4 plates and top each with the asparagus, eggs, and bacon. Drizzle with the remaining warm dressing.

NUTRITION (PER SERVING):

399 calories, **21 g protein**, 13 g carbohydrates, 4 g fiber, 5 g sugars, 29 g fat, 6 g saturated fat, 736 mg sodium

Huevos Rancheros Jars

PREP TIME: 5 minutes **TOTAL TIME:** 15 minutes Serves 2

3 eggs
1 cup salsa verde
½ avocado
1 clove garlic, chopped
juice of ½ lime
1 cup canned pinto beans
1 scallion, sliced
¼ cup cilantro
1 cup crumbled baked tortilla chips

Scramble the eggs in a small nonstick skillet over medium heat, until set, about 4 minutes. In a blender, puree the salsa verde, avocado, garlic, and lime juice. Divide the avocado sauce among 2 wide-mouth jars, and layer into each jar ½ cup of the beans, half the scrambled eggs, ½ sliced scallion, 2 tablespoons cilantro, and ½ cup of the chips. Seal shut and chill. Eat cold or reheat in the microwave for 30 seconds to 1 minute.

NUTRITION (PER SERVING):

424 calories, **18 g protein**, 47 g carbohydrates, 10 g fiber, 6 g sugar, 19 g total fat, 4 g saturated fat, 1299 mg sodium

Horseradish-Chive Scrambled Eggs with Lox on a Pumpernickel Bagel

Horseradish-Chive Scrambled Eggs with Lox on a Pumpernickel Bagel

PREP TIME: 5 minutes **TOTAL TIME:** 10 minutes Serves 1

2 eggs

½ teaspoon prepared horseradish

Pinch of kosher salt and ground black pepper

1 tablespoon thinly sliced chives

½ pumpernickel bagel, toasted

2 ounces (about 5 slices) lox

Beat the eggs with the horseradish and a pinch of salt and pepper. In a sprayed nonstick skillet, over medium-low heat, cook the eggs, stirring constantly, until large soft curds form and the eggs are cooked through, about 4 minutes. Off heat, stir in the chives. Layer the bagel half with the lox. Top with the eggs.

NUTRITION (PER SERVING):

506 calories, **53 g protein**, 34 g carbohydrates, 3 g fiber, 6 g sugar, 17 g fat, 5 g saturated fat, 637 mg sodium

Hummus Deviled Eggs

PREP TIME: 5 minutes **TOTAL TIME:** 10 minutes Serves 1

3 hard-boiled eggs

1 tablespoon prepared hummus

1 tablespoon fresh lemon juice

¼ teaspoon lemon zest

Kosher salt

1 tablespoon chopped fresh parsley

Ground black pepper, to taste

Slice the eggs lengthwise and transfer the yolks to a small bowl. Mash the yolks with the hummus, lemon juice and zest, and a pinch of salt. Spoon the mixture back into the whites. Sprinkle with the parsley and black pepper.

NUTRITION (PER SERVING):

265 calories, **20 g protein**, 6 g carbohydrates, 1 g fiber, 2 g sugar, 18 g fat, 5 g saturated fat, 488 mg sodium

TRY THESE TASTY VARIATIONS

Classic

Mash the yolks with 1 tablespoon mayonnaise, ¼ teaspoon Dijon mustard, and a dash hot sauce until smooth. Season to taste with salt and pepper. Sprinkle with ⅛ teaspoon paprika and 1 teaspoon thinly sliced chives.

NUTRITION (PER SERVING): 335 CALORIES, **19 G PROTEIN**, 2 G CARBOHYDRATES, 0 G FIBER, 2 G SUGAR, 27 G FAT, 6 G SATURATED FAT, 411 MG SODIUM

Smoked Salmon and Dill

Combine the yolks with 1 ounce finely diced cold smoked salmon, 1 tablespoon mayonnaise, 1 tablespoon diced shallot, 2 teaspoons chopped dill, 1 tablespoon lemon juice, and a few grinds black pepper. Top with more chopped dill.

NUTRITION (PER SERVING): 445 CALORIES, **37 G PROTEIN**, 6 G CARBOHYDRATES, 1 G FIBER, 3 G SUGAR, 30 G FAT, 7 G SATURATED FAT, 279 MG SODIUM

Avocado Lime

Mash the yolks with ¼ avocado, ½ teaspoon lime juice, and ⅛ teaspoon each ground cumin, onion powder, and garlic powder until smooth. Season to taste with salt and pepper. Top with 1 tablespoon chopped cilantro.

NUTRITION (PER SERVING): 317 CALORIES, **20 G PROTEIN**, 7 G CARBOHYDRATES, 4 G FIBER, 2 G SUGAR, 23 G FAT, 6 G SATURATED FAT, 431 MG SODIUM

Pesto Deviled Eggs

Mash the yolks with 1 tablespoon prepared pesto and 1 teaspoon olive oil and stir until smooth. Top with 1 teaspoon Parmesan cheese.

NUTRITION (PER SERVING): 298 CALORIES, **21 G PROTEIN**, 4 G CARBOHYDRATES, 0 G FIBER, 0 G SUGAR, 24 G FAT, 6 G SATURATED FAT, 301 MG SODIUM

Sweet Berry Omelets

PREP TIME: 5 minutes **TOTAL TIME:** 15 minutes Serves 2

3 large eggs

¼ teaspoon vanilla extract

¾ cup fresh or frozen and thawed blueberries

1 tablespoon part-skim ricotta cheese

1 tablespoon chopped toasted pecans

Sprinkle of cinnamon

1. In a small bowl, mix the eggs with the vanilla until the eggs are frothy. Coat small nonstick skillet with cooking spray. Cook the eggs over medium heat until set, about 1 to 2 minutes. Flip and cook until no longer runny, about 1 minute more. Transfer to a plate.

2. Spray the skillet with more cooking spray, and cook the blueberries over medium-high heat, until the fruit is heated through. Top half the omelet with the ricotta, pecans, and the berries; fold over the other half. Sprinkle with the cinnamon.

NUTRITION (PER SERVING):

350 calories, **22 g protein**, 19 g carbohydrates, 4 g fiber, 12 g sugar, 21 g fat, 6 g saturated fat, 234 mg sodium

Salmon Kedgeree

PREP TIME: 5 minutes **TOTAL TIME:** 25 minutes Serves 2

⅓ cup brown lentils

½ stick cinnamon

2 cups water

Kosher salt

½ cup basmati rice

2 tablespoons unsalted butter

½ medium onion, chopped

1 jalapeño, diced and seeded

2 teaspoons minced ginger

1 clove garlic, minced

1½ teaspoons Madras curry powder

1 can (6 ounces) salmon, drained and flaked

¼ cup frozen peas

1 tablespoon lemon juice

2 hard-boiled eggs, chopped

¼ cup cilantro, chopped

1. In a medium pot, combine the lentils, cinnamon stick, water, and a pinch of salt; bring to a boil. Stir in the rice, reduce the heat to a gentle simmer, cover, and cook until the rice is tender, about 15 minutes.

2. Meanwhile, in a large skillet over medium, melt the butter and cook the onion, jalapeño, ginger, garlic, and curry powder until all the vegetables are tender, about 7 minutes. Add the rice to the onion mixture, stirring until everything is combined. Add the salmon to the lentil mixture with the peas and lemon juice. Stir until everything is heated through and combined, about 2 minutes. Add the eggs and cilantro and serve.

NUTRITION (PER SERVING):

538 calories, **35 g protein**, 54 g carbohydrates, 9 g fiber, 3 g sugar, 20 g fat, 9 g saturated fat, 552 mg sodium

Pesto Frittata Muffins

PREP TIME: 5 minutes **TOTAL TIME:** 30 minutes Serves 4

4 slices bacon

8 eggs

⅓ cup sour cream

⅓ cup chopped sun-dried tomatoes

3 tablespoons pesto

½ teaspoon kosher salt

¼ teaspoon crushed red pepper flakes

3 tablespoons shredded mozzarella cheese

Chopped chives

1. Heat the oven to 375°F. Spray 12 muffin cups with cooking spray.

2. Put the bacon in a large skillet over mediumheat. Cook the bacon, turning once, until crispy, about 8 minutes. Remove to a paper towel–lined plate. When cool enough to handle, crumble.

3. In a large bowl, whisk together the eggs, sour cream, sun-dried tomatoes, pesto, salt, red pepper flakes, and bacon. Pour into the muffin cups, sprinkle with the cheese, and bake until the eggs are set, about 20 minutes. Sprinkle with the chopped chives.

NUTRITION (PER SERVING):

310 calories, **20 g protein**, 5 g carbohydrates, 1 g fiber, 3 g sugar, 23 g fat, 8.5 g saturated fat, 666 mg sodium

Kale Salad with Tomato Caesar Dressing

PREP TIME: 10 minutes **TOTAL TIME:** 20 minutes Serves 6

⅓ cup mayonnaise

2 hard-boiled eggs

¼ cup oil-packed sun-dried tomatoes

1 teaspoon lemon zest

Juice of ½ lemon

2 teaspoons coarse-ground Dijon mustard

4 anchovy fillets

2 cloves garlic

Kosher salt and ground black pepper

⅓ cup olive oil

1 bunch kale, leaves stripped from stems and coarsely chopped

1. In a food processor or blender, blend together the mayonnaise, egg, tomatoes, lemon zest, lemon juice, mustard, anchovies, garlic, and a generous pinch of salt and pepper. With machine running, drizzle in olive oil.

2. Place the kale into a large bowl. Pour the dressing over it and massage the dressing into the kale until wilted, at least 5 minutes.

NUTRITION (PER SERVING):

277 calories, **6 g protein**, 9 g carbohydrates, 2 g fiber, 0 g sugar, 26 g fat, 4 g saturated fat, 305 mg sodium

Southwest Breakfast Burritos

PREP TIME: 10 minutes **TOTAL TIME:** 40 minutes Serves 4

8 eggs

½ white onion, chopped

½ red bell pepper, chopped

1 can (4 ounces) chopped green chile peppers, drained

½ teaspoon ground black pepper

¼ teaspoon kosher salt

1 tablespoon olive oil

4 whole wheat tortillas (8" diameter)

1 can (15 ounce) black beans, drained and rinsed

½ cup shredded cheddar cheese

½ cup all-natural salsa

1. Heat an oven to 350°F. In a large bowl, whisk together the eggs, onion, bell pepper, green chiles, black pepper, and salt until combined.

2. In a large nonstick skillet, heat the oil over over medium heat. Pour in the egg mixture and scramble the eggs until set but still moist, about 8 minutes. Remove from the heat and set aside.

3. Prepare an assembly line with all ingredients. Assemble each burrito by placing a quarter each of the eggs, beans, cheese, and salsa, on the bottom half of the tortilla. Fold in the left and right sides then roll up the burrito. Wrap the burritos tightly in foil and bake until the cheese is melted and the beans are heated through, about 10 minutes.

Note: Burritos can be frozen after wrapped in foil for up to 3 months. Bake in a 350°F until heated through, about 30 minutes or remove foil, wrap in paper towels and microwave on high for up to 3 minutes.

NUTRITION (PER SERVING):

460 calories, **26 g protein**, 42 g carbohydrates, 9 g fiber, 4 g sugar, 21 g fat, 8 g saturated fat, 959 mg sodium

Cheese and Egg
Quesadillas

Cheese and Egg Quesadillas

PREP TIME: 10 minutes **TOTAL TIME:** 25 minutes Serves 2

⅓ tablespoon butter

½ red bell pepper, finely chopped

2 scallions, finely chopped

4 eggs

¼ cup milk

½ cup shredded cheese such as Cheddar, Swiss or horseradish, divided

2 flour tortillas, (7-8 inches each)

1. In a large skillet over medium heat, melt the butter. Cook the pepper and scallions, stirring frequently, until tender, about 5 minutes. In a small bowl, whisk together the eggs and milk. Pour into the skillet and add ¼ cup of the cheese. Cook, stirring frequently, until the mixture is scrambled and the eggs are cooked through but still moist. Cover and set aside.

2. Spray a medium skillet with cooking spray and place over medium heat. Place 1 tortilla in the skillet and sprinkle with 1 tablespoon of the remaining cheese. Add half of the egg mixture to half of the tortilla and sprinkle with 1 tablespoon of cheese. Fold the empty half over the eggs and cheese. Cook until the cheese is melted, 2 minutes. Turn over and cook 1 minute more. Repeat with the remaining tortilla and eggs.

NUTRITION (PER SERVING):
474 calories, **24 g protein**, 31 g carbohydrates, 2 g fiber, 6 g sugar, 28 g fat, 14 g saturated fat, 716 mg sodium

Greek Salad Pasta

Flavorful Chicken BREASTS That Never Bore

Greek Salad Pasta

PREP TIME: 10 minutes **TOTAL TIME:** 30 minutes Serves 4

½ pound orecchiette

4 thin sliced chicken cutlets (about 12 ounces total)

Kosher salt and ground black pepper

3 tablespoons extra-virgin olive oil

2 tablespoons red wine vinegar

1 teaspoon dried oregano

Kosher salt and ground black pepper

½ English cucumber, cut into half moons

1 cup halved cherry tomatoes

½ cup pitted kalamata olives

½ small red onion, thinly sliced

¼ cup crumbled feta cheese

1 tablespoon chopped fresh dill

1. Bring a pot of well-salted water to a boil. Cook the pasta according to package directions. Season the chicken with salt and pepper. Heat a grill pan over medium high and spray the grill pan with cooking spray. Add the chicken and cook until good grill marks form, about 5 minutes. Flip and continue to cook until cooked through, about 4 minutes more. Transfer the chicken to a cutting board and cut into bite size pieces.

2. In a large bowl, whisk together the olive oil, vinegar, oregano, a pinch of salt, and a few grinds of pepper. Add the cucumber, tomatoes, olives, onion, feta, and dill. Drain the pasta and toss into the vegetables in the bowl with the chicken to combine. Season to taste with salt and pepper and serve hot, cold, or room temperature.

NUTRITION (PER SERVING):
550 calories, **28 g protein**, 49 g carbohydrates, 4 g fiber, 3 g sugar, 26 g fat, 5 g saturated fat, 979 mg sodium

Herb Pounded Chicken
with Arugula

Herb-Pounded Chicken with Arugula

PREP TIME: 5 minutes **TOTAL TIME:** 30 minutes Serves 2

2 (6 ounces to 8 ounces each) boneless skinless chicken breasts

3 tablespoons extra-virgin olive oil

1 small lemon, zested plus wedges for serving

2 teaspoons chopped fresh thyme

1 teaspoon chopped fresh rosemary

1 small clove garlic, chopped

¼ teaspoon crushed red pepper

Kosher salt

2 cups arugula

¼ red onion, thinly sliced

1 teaspoon balsamic vinegar

1. Starting at the thicker side, make a lengthwise cut into the side of the chicken breasts about two-thirds of the way in. Fold the breasts open like a book.

2. In a bowl, mix 1 tablespoon of the oil, lemon zest, thyme, rosemary, garlic, crushed red pepper flakes, and a big pinch of salt. Rub this mixture all over the chicken. Place the each chicken breast between two pieces of plastic wrap and using a meat mallet (or bottom of a heavy pan), pound the breasts to a ¼-inch thickness.

3. In a large skillet over medium-high heat, heat 1 tablespoon olive oil. Add a chicken breast and sear on both sides, about 3 minutes each. Transfer to a plate and repeat with the other breast.

4. In a medium bowl, toss the arugula, onion, balsamic and the remaining 1 tablespoon olive oil. Squeeze a wedge of lemon over the chicken and serve with the arugula salad.

NUTRITION (PER SERVING):

401 calories, **37 g protein**, 4 g carbohydrates, 1 g fiber, 2 g sugar, 27 g fat, 4 g saturated fat, 349 mg sodium

Curry Mint Chicken with Butternut Squash

PREP TIME: 10 minutes **TOTAL TIME:** 30 minutes Serves 2

2 (6 ounces to 8 ounces each) boneless skinless chicken breast

Kosher salt and ground black pepper

2 teaspoons yellow curry powder

1 tablespoon olive oil

4 cups diced butternut squash

2 small garlic clove, minced

1 medium shallot, minced

2 tablespoon chopped roasted almonds

¼ cup low-sodium chicken broth

¼ cup coarsely chopped fresh mint

¼ cup coarsely chopped fresh basil

1. Heat the oven to 350°F. Season the chicken with a good pinch each of salt and pepper, plus ½ teaspoon curry powder. In a large ovenproof skillet over medium heat, heat the oil. Add the chicken and sear each side until browned, about 2 minutes per side. Add the squash, garlic, shallot, almonds, the rest of the curry powder, plus a pinch each of salt and pepper and cook for 1 minute.

2. Cover with a lid, and place it in the oven. Roast until the chicken is cooked through and the vegetables are tender, 10 to 12 minutes.

3. Remove the pan from the oven; remove the lid. Add the chicken broth, mint and basil. Transfer everything to a bowl.

NUTRITION (PER SERVING):

453 calories, **42 g protein**, 41 g carbohydrates, 8 g fiber, 8 g sugar, 15 g fat, 2 g saturated fat, 539 mg sodium

Poached Chicken with White Bean and Watercress Salad

PREP TIME: 5 minutes **TOTAL TIME:** 25 minutes Serves 2

2 (6 ounces to 8 ounces each) boneless skinless chicken breasts

Kosher salt

1 lemon, halved and juiced, rinds reserved

2 teaspoons Dijon mustard

1 tablespoon extra-virgin olive oil

1 bunch watercress, chopped

1 can (15 ounces) white beans, drained and rinsed

1 pint cherry tomatoes, halved

5 kalamata olives, pitted and chopped

Ground black pepper

1. In a pot filled halfway with cold water, add the chicken, plus 2 tablespoons kosher salt. Adjust the heat to medium and add the lemon rind. When the water begins to simmer, turn off the heat, cover the pot, and sit 5 minutes.

2. Meanwhile, in a small bowl, mix the mustard, oil, lemon juice, and a pinch of salt.

3. Remove the chicken from the poaching liquid, cut into bite-sized pieces, and mix with the watercress, beans, tomatoes, and olives. Toss with the dressing and freshly ground black pepper.

NUTRITION (PER SERVING):

431 calories, **45 g protein**, 28 g carbohydrates, 8 g fiber, 6 g sugar, 15 g fat, 2 g saturated fat, 970 mg sodium

Light and Lemony Chicken Salad

PREP TIME: 10 minutes **TOTAL TIME:** 55 minutes (with cooling time) Serves 4

2 boneless, skinless chicken breasts (about 1 pound)

1 cup grapes, halved

1 small apple, diced

¾ cup plain nonfat Greek yogurt

½ cup pistachios, toasted and chopped

1 large stalk celery, sliced

1 small shallot, minced

3 tablespoons fresh lemon juice

½ teaspoon kosher salt

½ teaspoon ground black pepper

4 cups spring mix

¼ cup chopped mint leaves

4 lemon wedges

1. Place the chicken in a medium saucepan and add enough water to cover by 1-inch. Bring to a simmer over medium-high heat, reduce heat to medium-low, and cook until they register 160°F on an instant-read thermometer, about 15 minutes. Transfer chicken breasts to a bowl and cover with some of the cooking liquid. Refrigerate until cold.

2. Shred the chicken breasts and drain the excess liquid. In a medium bowl, toss with the grapes, apple, yogurt, pistachios, celery, shallot, lemon juice, salt, and pepper. Serve over salad greens topped with mint leaves and lemon wedges.

NUTRITION (PER SERVING):

307 calories, **33 g protein**, 23 g carbohydrates, 5 g fiber, 13 g sugars, 10 g fat, 1.5 g saturated fat, 518 mg sodium

Orange Chicken and Broccoli Stir-Fry

PREP TIME: 5 minutes **TOTAL TIME:** 20 minutes Serves 2

¼ cup fresh orange juice

1 tablespoon reduced-sodium soy sauce

1 tablespoon orange marmalade

1 teaspoon cornstarch

2 tablespoons canola oil

½ pound chicken tenders, trimmed and cut into 1-inch pieces

1 scallion, thinly sliced, whites and greens kept separate

1 large clove garlic, minced

1½ teaspoons minced fresh ginger

Pinch of crushed red-pepper flakes

¼ cup reduced-sodium chicken broth

1 pound broccoli crowns, chopped into florets

½ red bell pepper, thinly sliced

1½ cups cooked brown rice

1. In a small bowl, combine the juice, soy sauce, marmalade, and cornstarch. Stir until blended. Set aside.

2. In a wok or large nonstick skillet, heat the oil over medium-high heat. Add the chicken and cook, stirring frequently, until cooked through, about 5 minutes. Add the scallion whites, garlic, ginger, and red-pepper flakes and stir to combine. With a slotted spoon, remove chicken to plate.

3. Reduce the heat to medium. Add the broth and broccoli to the wok. Cover and cook 2 minutes. Increase the heat to high and add bell pepper. Cook, stirring frequently, until the broth evaporates and the vegetables are crisp-tender, about 2 minutes. Stir the sauce and add to the wok along with the chicken. Cook, stirring constantly, until the sauce thickens, about 2 minutes. Serve over the rice and sprinkle with the scallion greens.

NUTRITION (PER SERVING):

540 calories, **36 g protein**, 60 g carbohydrates, 11 g fiber, 11 g sugar, 19 g fat, 2 g saturated fat, 475 mg sodium

Orange Chicken and
Broccoli Stir-Fry

Pan Roasted Chicken with Mushroom and Herb Gravy

PREP TIME: 10 minutes **TOTAL TIME:** 45 minutes Serves 4

2 teaspoons olive oil

4 thyme sprigs, plus 2 teaspoons chopped thyme leaves

4 bone-in, skin-on chicken breasts (about 2 pounds)

½ teaspoon kosher salt

½ teaspoon ground black pepper

6 ounces shiitake mushrooms, trimmed and sliced

2 shallots, finely diced

4 teaspoons all-purpose flour

¼ cup white wine

1½ cups low-sodium chicken broth

1. Heat the oven to 425°F. In a large ovenproof skillet, heat the oil and thyme sprigs over medium-high heat.

2. Season the chicken with salt and pepper and add to the pan, skin side down. Cook until the skin is crisp and golden, about 4 minutes. Flip the breasts, transfer the pan to the oven, and roast until a meat thermometer registers 160°F when inserted into the thickest part without touching the bone, about 20 minutes. Carefully remove the pan from the oven and transfer the chicken to a platter.

3. Place the pan over medium high heat and cook the mushrooms until tender, adding 1 to 2 tablespoons broth, if pan seems dry, about 5 minutes. Add the shallots and cook until softened, about 3 minutes. Stir in the flour and cook 1 minute. Add the wine, scraping the bottom of the pan, and cook until only 2 tablespoons wine remain, about 2 minutes. Add the broth and cook until the mixture thickens, about 3 minutes. Stir in the fresh thyme, season to taste with salt and pepper, and serve with the chicken.

NUTRITION (PER SERVING):

253 calories, **34 g protein**, 11 g carbohydrates, 2 g fiber, 4 g sugars, 6 g fat, 1 g saturated fat, 446 mg sodium

Chicken Pot Pie Stew

PREP TIME: 5 minutes **TOTAL TIME:** 50 minutes Serves 4

1 tablespoon olive oil, divided

8 ounces sliced mushrooms

2 boneless, skinless chicken breasts, chopped into 1-inch pieces

1 container (7 to 8 ounces) store bought diced onion, carrot, and celery (mirepoix)

2 sprigs fresh thyme

1 quart low-sodium chicken broth

1 can (12 ounces) evaporated milk

3 tablespoons white whole wheat flour

1 cup frozen peas

¼ cup chopped fresh parsley

1. In a medium pot, heat half the oil over medium high heat. Add the mushrooms and cook until browned, about 5 minutes. Remove from the pot and transfer to a plate.

2. Heat the remaining oil, add the chicken, and cook until browned on all sides, about 8 minutes. Transfer to plate with mushrooms. Add onion, celery, and thyme and cook until tender, about 4 minutes.

3. Add the broth, mushrooms, and chicken to pot, bring to a simmer, and cook until the chicken is cooked through and tender, about 6 minutes.

4. Whisk together milk and flour, add to pot and bring to a simmer. Add peas and bring to a simmer. Cook until mixture is slightly thickened, about 4 minutes.

5. Remove the thyme sprigs and discard. Stir in parsley and season to taste with salt and pepper.

NUTRITION (PER SERVING):

342 calories, **28 g protein**, 29 g carbohydrates, 5 g fiber, 15 g sugar, 13 g fat, 5 g saturated fat, 438 mg sodium

Char Siu Chicken

PREP TIME: 5 minutes **TOTAL TIME:** 50 minutes Serves 4 as a main or 8 as an appetizer

2 tablespoons low sodium soy sauce

2 tablespoons hoisin sauce

1 teaspoon brown sugar

¼ teaspoon five spice powder

¼ teaspoon beet powder (for color; optional)

1 pound boneless skinless chicken breasts, cut into 1-inch pieces

1 large zucchini, cut into 1-inch pieces

8 bamboo skewers, soaked in water

1. In a medium bowl, mix the soy sauce, hoisin, brown sugar, five spice powder, and beet powder, if using. Set aside 2 tablespoons; add the chicken to the remaining soy mixture and toss to coat. Cover and refrigerate for at least 30 minutes and up to 1 hour.

2. Heat a grill or grill pan to medium hot. Alternately thread the chicken and zucchini on the skewers. Grill the skewers, turning once, until just cooked through (165°F on an instant read thermometer), 5 to 6 minutes per side. In the last minute of cooking, brush some of the reserved sauce over the skewers. Alternatively, you can broil the skewers, about 4 minutes per side.

Note: This sweet-savory chicken has a characteristic bright red hue, which you can get from beet powder instead of food coloring. Serve with a green salad.

NUTRITION (PER SERVING AS A MAIN):

169 calories, **26 g protein**, 8 g carbohydrates, 1 g fiber, 5 g sugar, 4 g fat, 1 g saturated fat, 534 mg sodium

Apple and Chicken Curry

PREP TIME: 10 minutes **TOTAL TIME:** 40 minutes Serves 4

1 tablespoon olive oil

1 medium yellow onion, diced

2 cloves garlic, minced

1 tablespoon grated ginger

1¼ pounds boneless skinless chicken breast, cut into 1½-inch cubes

Kosher salt and freshly ground black pepper

1 medium tomato, diced

1 tablespoon curry powder

2 sweet tart apples, cored and cut into 1-inch cubes

¾ cup low-sodium chicken broth

¼ cup coconut milk

4 ounces baby spinach

2 cups cooked brown rice or multi colored quinoa

In a large nonstick skillet, heat the oil over medium until shimmering. Add the onion and cook until tender, about 5 minutes. Stir in the garlic and ginger, cook until fragrant, about 1 minute. Season the chicken generously with salt and pepper; add to the pan and cook until golden, about 5 minutes. Stir in the tomato and curry, and cook until fragrant, about 1 minute. Add the apples, broth, and coconut milk and simmer until the sauce thickens slightly and the chicken is completely cooked through, about 10 minutes. Stir in the spinach until wilted, and season to taste with salt and pepper. Serves over the rice or quinoa.

NUTRITION (PER SERVING):
419 calories, **36 g protein**, 44 g carbohydrates, 7 g fiber, 12 g sugar, 12 g fat, 4 saturated fat, 355 sodium

Slow Cooker BBQ Pulled Chicken Flatbreads

Slow Cooker BBQ Pulled Chicken Flatbreads

PREP TIME: 15 minutes **TOTAL TIME:** 4 hours Serves 2

¾ cup crushed tomatoes

2 tablespoons apple cider vinegar

1 tablespoon molasses

1 teaspoon smoked or sweet paprika

1 teaspoon Dijon mustard, divided

¼ teaspoon sea salt

¼ teaspoon ground black pepper, divided

1 small red onion, thinly sliced, divided

8 ounces boneless skinless chicken breast

1½ cups shredded cabbage

1 large carrot, grated

2 tablespoons dill pickle juice

1 tablespoon mayonnaise

4 small whole wheat flatbreads or pita

1. In a slow cooker, combine the tomatoes, vinegar, molasses, paprika, half the mustard, salt, and half the pepper. Whisk until smooth. Add half of the onion and all of the chicken to the slow cooker, tossing to combine. Cover and cook on low for about 3 ½ hours, until the chicken is very tender and reaches an internal temperature of 165°F. (You should be able to pull the chicken apart with a fork.)

2. Meanwhile, in a large bowl, combine the cabbage, carrot, pickle juice, mayonnaise, the remaining onion, mustard and pepper. Cover and refrigerate the coleslaw until ready to serve.

3. Remove the chicken from the sauce and place it on a cutting board. Shred it with two forks and return it to the slow cooker. Mix until the chicken is evenly coated. Divide the chicken and slaw among the flatbreads or pita.

Note: Pulled chicken freezes well, and this recipe doubles easily. Make a big batch and freeze half for a fast weeknight dinner.

NUTRITION (PER SERVING):

447 calories, **33 g protein**, 60 g carbohydrates, 9 g fiber, 17 g sugar, 10 g fat, 2 g saturated fat, 816 mg sodium

Grilled Honey-Dijon Chicken Sandwiches

PREP TIME: 5 minutes **TOTAL TIME:** 90 minutes Serves 6

⅓ cup Dijon mustard

⅓ cup honey

Juice of half a lemon (1 to 2 tablespoons)

½ teaspoon paprika

¼ teaspoon kosher salt

½ teaspoon dried thyme

⅛ teaspoon crushed red pepper flakes (optional)

6 chicken cutlets (about 12 ounces)

6 whole wheat hamburger buns

6 slices Swiss cheese

6 cooked bacon slices

Lettuce and tomato slices (optional)

1. In a large mixing bowl, combine the mustard and honey. Add the lemon juice, paprika, salt, thyme, and red-pepper flakes, if using. Stir to combine.

2. Add the chicken to the marinade and turn to coat. Cover and marinate in the refrigerator for at least an hour and up to 24 hours.

3. Heat a grill or grill pan to medium. Remove the chicken from the marinade and cook, flipping once, until a thermometer inserted in the thickest portion registers 165°F, about 8 minutes.

4. Transfer the marinade to a small saucepan. Bring to a boil over medium-high heat and cook until thickened, about 5 minutes. Remove from the heat and set aside.

5. On the bottom half of each bun, place a piece of chicken, a slice of cheese, a slice of bacon, a drizzle of the cooked marinade, and lettuce and tomato, if using.

NUTRITION (PER SERVING):

400 calories, **26 g protein**, 42 g carbohydrates, 3 g fiber, 20 g sugar, 15 g fat, 7 g saturated fat, 882 mg sodium

Chicken Parmesan Sliders

PREP TIME: 5 minutes **TOTAL TIME:** 3¼ hours Serves 6

1½ pounds boneless skinless chicken breasts

1 jar (28 ounces) all-natural marinara sauce

12 mini wheat buns or dinner rolls

¼ cup freshly grated Parmesan cheese

2 slices provolone or mozzarella cheese, cut into thirds

1. Combine the chicken and marinara sauce in a slow cooker and cook on low until the chicken is cooked through and an instant read thermometer registers 165°F, 3 to 4 hours. Using 2 forks, shred the chicken and toss with the sauce to coat.

2. Heat the oven to broil. On a large baking sheet divide the shredded chicken among the bottom of the buns, sprinkle each with 2 teaspoons of Parmesan cheese, top with 1 piece of provolone, and place the top of the bun on the baking sheet beside it. Broil until the cheese melts and the bread toasts slightly, about 2 minutes. Place the top bun on the sandwich and serve.

NUTRITION (PER SERVING):

348 calories, **37 g protein**, 30 g carbohydrates, 5 g fiber, 3 g sugar, 11 g fat, 3.5 g saturated fat, 997 mg sodium

Chicken Parmesan Sliders

Chicken Cordon Bleu

PREP TIME: 5 minutes **TOTAL TIME:** 40 minutes Serves 4

- **4 chicken cutlets (about 12 ounces total)**
- **Kosher salt and ground black pepper**
- **4 thin slices black forest ham**
- **4 thin slices Swiss cheese**
- **¼ cup all purpose flour**
- **2 tablespoons unsalted butter**
- **1 tablespoon olive oil**
- **8 ounces sliced mixed mushrooms**
- **1 thinly sliced shallot**
- **½ cup white wine**

1. Heat the oven to 400°F. Lay the chicken cutlets on a work surface and season both sides with salt and pepper. Lay 1 slice ham and Swiss cheese over each cutlet. Roll each cutlet and secure the end with a toothpick. Place the flour in a small bowl and place each chicken roll in the center of the flour and coat all over.

2. Melt the butter and oil together in a large oven safe skillet. When the foaming subsides add the chicken and sear until golden on 4 sides, about 3 minutes per side. Remove to a plate and add the mushrooms and shallots to the skillet. Cook, stirring, until the mushrooms have released their liquid and are slightly golden, about 5 minutes. Pour in the wine and scrape up all the browned bits in the pan. Place the chicken in the pan, nestled among the mushrooms, and roast in the oven until the chicken is completely cooked through and an instant read thermometer registers 165°, about 10 minutes.

3. Serve the chicken with the mushroom sauce spooned over the top.

NUTRITION (PER SERVING):

312 calories, **27 g protein**, 10 g carbohydrates, 1 g fiber, 2 g sugar, 16 g fat, 7 saturated fat, 452 sodium

Oven Baked Chicken Fingers

PREP TIME: 5 minutes **TOTAL TIME:** 35 minutes Serves 4

1 pound chicken tenders
Kosher salt
½ teaspoon garlic powder
¼ cup all purpose flour
1 egg, beaten with 1 tablespoon of water
½ cup panko breadcrumbs
¼ cup finely grated Parmesan cheese

1. Heat oven to 425°F. Line a large rimmed baking sheet with foil and mist with cooking spray. Season the chicken all over with salt and the garlic powder.

2. In 3 separate shallow dishes, place the flour, egg, and panko mixed with Parmesan. Coat the chicken first with flour, then egg, then the cheesy breadcrumbs and transfer to the prepared baking sheet. Mist the coated chicken with cooking spray.

3. Bake, flipping once, until the chicken is cooked through, an instant read thermometer registers 165°, and the coating is golden brown, about 20 minutes. Serve with your favorite dipping sauce.

NUTRITION (PER SERVING):
226 calories, **29 g protein**, 12 g carbohydrates, 1 g fiber, 0 g sugar, 6 g fat, 2 g saturated fat, 487 mg sodium

Chicken Pad Thai

PREP TIME: 5 minutes **TOTAL TIME:** 20 minutes Serves 4

4 ounces flat brown rice noodles
2 tablespoons low-sodium soy sauce
2 tablespoons peanut butter
1 tablespoon Sriracha sauce
1 teaspoon fish sauce
1 tablespoon peanut oil
1 pound boneless, skinless chicken breasts, cut into 1½-inch strips
2 cloves garlic, minced
3 scallions, sliced
1 cup bean sprouts
¼ cup peanuts, chopped
1 lime, quartered, for garnish

Prepare the noodles according to package directions. In a small bowl, combine the soy sauce, peanut butter, Sriracha, and fish sauce. In a large nonstick skillet, heat the oil over medium-high heat. Cook the chicken, stirring often, until no longer pink, about 5 minutes. Add the garlic and cook for 30 seconds. Stir in the noodles and cook until hot, 1 minute. Add the soy sauce mixture and cook, tossing, for 1 minute. Stir in the scallions and remove from the heat. Divide among 4 plates, garnishing each with a quarter of the bean sprouts and peanuts. Serve with the lime wedges.

NUTRITION (PER SERVING):
386 calories, **32 g protein**, 30 g carbohydrates, 4 g fiber, 4 g sugar, 15 g fat, 3 g saturated fat, 692 mg sodium

YUMMY THIGHS, WINGS, DRUMSTICKS

Simple Chicken and Bean Soup

PREP TIME: 5 minutes **TOTAL TIME:** 45 minutes Serves 6

1 tablespoon olive oil

1 onion, diced

2 carrots, chopped

3 cloves garlic, smashed

1 quart low-sodium chicken broth

1 pound boneless, skinless chicken thighs

1 can (15 ounces) cannellini beans, rinsed and drained

1 bag (5 ounces) baby spinach

Kosher salt and black pepper

2 tablespoons grated Parmesan

Heat the olive oil in a large pot over medium. Add the onion, carrots, and garlic, and cook until softened, about 5 minutes. Add the broth, chicken, and beans. Bring to a boil, turn the heat to low and simmer, covered, until the chicken is cooked through, about 20 minutes. Remove the chicken from the soup and use two forks to shred. Return the chicken to the soup. Add the spinach and season to taste with salt and pepper. Ladle into soup bowls and top with Parmesan.

NUTRITION (PER SERVING):

206 calories, **21 g protein**, 15 g carbohydrates, 4 g fiber, 2 g sugar, 7 g fat, 2 g saturated fat, 392 mg sodium

Simple Chicken
and Bean Soup

Simple Chicken and Veggie Stir Fry

PREP TIME: 20 minutes **TOTAL TIME:** 30 minutes Serves 4

⅓ cup low-sodium soy sauce

2 tablespoons honey

2 tablespoons cornstarch

1½ teaspoons sesame oil

2 tablespoons peanut oil, divided

1 pound boneless, skinless chicken thighs, thinly sliced

1-inch piece ginger, peeled and thinly sliced

2 cloves garlic, thinly sliced

1 small red onion, cut into 1-inch pieces

1 red bell pepper, cut into 1-inch pieces

1 cup broccoli florets

1 cup cauliflower florets

1 cup sugar snap peas, halved crosswise

2 scallions, thinly sliced, for garnish

Sesame seeds, toasted, for garnish

2 cups of your favorite cooked grain (optional)

1. In a small bowl, whisk together the soy sauce, honey, cornstarch, and sesame oil.

2. Heat 1 tablespoon peanut oil in a wok or large skillet over high. Add the chicken and cook, stirring often, until browned and cooked through, 3 minutes. Transfer to a plate.

3. Add the remaining oil to the wok. Add the ginger and garlic and cook until fragrant, about 30 seconds. Add the onion, bell pepper, broccoli, cauliflower, and peas, and cook, stirring constantly, until bright and crisp-tender, about 2 minutes. Return the chicken to wok, pour over the soy sauce mixture, and cook, stirring constantly, until the sauce has thickened and the flavors have melded, about 2 minutes more.

4. Serve garnished with scallions and sesame seeds, over grain, if using.

NUTRITION (PER SERVING):
305 calories, **25 g protein**, 22 g carbohydrates, 3 g fiber, 12 g sugar, 13 g fat, 3 g saturated fat, 828 mg sodium

Slow Cooker Orange Chicken and Broccoli

PREP TIME: 5 minutes **TOTAL TIME:** 3 hours, 25 minutes Serves 4

1 cup low-sodium chicken broth

1 large orange, zested to yield 1 tablespoon, juiced to yield ½ cup

⅓ cup low-sodium soy sauce

¼ cup packed brown sugar

1 tablespoon grated fresh ginger

2 cloves garlic, minced or pressed

1 teaspoon crushed red pepper flakes

2 pounds boneless skinless chicken thighs, cut into 2-inch pieces

¼ cup cornstarch

Two bags (12 ounces each) fresh broccoli florets

Cooked brown rice, sliced scallions, and sesame seeds (optional)

1. In a 6-quart slow cooker, whisk together the broth, orange juice and zest, soy sauce, brown sugar, ginger, garlic, and red pepper flakes.

2. Toss the chicken in the cornstarch and stir into the sauce. Cover and cook on low until the chicken is cooked through and tender, 3 hours.

3. Stir in the broccoli and cook until bright green, about 20 minutes more. Season to taste with salt. Serve over brown rice, and sprinkle with scallions and sesame seeds, if desired.

NUTRITION (PER SERVING):

436 calories, **51 g protein**, 36 g carbohydrates, 6 g fiber, 16 g sugar, 10 g fat, 2.5 g saturated fat, 982 mg sodium

Pollo alla Calabrese

Pollo alla Calabrese

PREP TIME: 10 minutes **TOTAL TIME:** 1 hour Serves 4

8 bone-in, skin-on chicken thighs

1 pound red potatoes, cut into ½-inch wedges

1 pint cherry tomatoes, halves

3 red, orange, or yellow bell peppers, cut into ½-inch strips

1 large sweet onion, cut into ½-inch wedges

3 tablespoons olive oil

4 cloves garlic, minced

1 teaspoon dried oregano

1 teaspoon sweet paprika

1 teaspoon kosher salt

¼ teaspoon crushed red pepper flakes

Thinly sliced basil, for serving

1. Heat the oven to 400°F. On a large rimmed baking sheet, combine the chicken, potatoes, tomatoes, peppers, onion, oil, garlic, oregano, paprika, salt, and pepper flakes, tossing to combine and rubbing the chicken with the spices.

2. Arrange the vegetables underneath the chicken pieces. Roast until the vegetables are tender and the chicken is fully cooked through, about 45 minutes, turning the chicken and tossing the vegetables halfway through. Scatter basil over top to serve.

NUTRITION (PER SERVING):

408 calories, **31 g protein**, 34 g carbohydrates, 6 g fiber, 11 g sugars, 17 g total fat, 3 g saturated fat, 638 mg sodium

Spicy Sauteed Chicken with Kimchi

PREP TIME: 5 minutes **TOTAL TIME:** 35 minutes Serves 2

⅓ cup white rice

1 tablespoon olive oil

4 boneless skinless chicken thighs, cubed

1 jalapeño, seeded and thinly sliced (optional)

1 thumb-sized piece ginger, peeled and minced

1½ cups store-bought kimchi

½ teaspoon toasted sesame seeds

¼ sheet nori, crumbled

1. Cook the rice according to package directions.

2. In a nonstick skillet over medium, heat the olive oil. Add the chicken, jalapeño (if using), and ginger. Cook until the chicken is almost cooked through, about 5 minutes.

3. Add the kimchi and simmer until the sauce thickens and the chicken is cooked through and glazed, about 5 minutes.

4. Serve over the rice and top with the sesame seeds and nori.

NUTRITION (PER SERVING):

400 calories, **35 g protein**, 30 g carbohydrates, 7 g fiber, 0 g sugar, 13 g fat, 2.5 g saturated fat, 971 mg sodium

Moroccan Chicken Thighs

PREP TIME: 10 minutes **TOTAL TIME:** 30 minutes Serves 4

2 teaspoons ground turmeric

1 teaspoon ground cinnamon

½ teaspoon kosher salt

½ teaspoon ground black pepper

¼ teaspoon to ½ teaspoon crushed red pepper flakes

4 bone-in, skin-on chicken thighs (about 1 pound)

2 teaspoons olive oil

1 large yellow onion, chopped

1 clove garlic, minced

1 two-inch-piece of ginger, peeled and sliced into matchsticks

1 can (28 ounces) diced tomatoes

½ cup dried fruit, such as prunes, apricots, and raisins

Chopped parsley

1. In a small bowl, stir together the turmeric, cinnamon, salt, and black and red pepper. Rub the spice mixture all over the chicken thighs.

2. In a large Dutch oven or heavy duty pot, heat the oil over medium high heat. Add the chicken, skin side down, and cook until browned, 3 to 5 minutes. Flip the chicken, cook 1 minute more. Transfer the chicken to a plate.

3. Add the onion and cook until translucent, about 5 minutes. Add the garlic and ginger and cook until fragrant, about 30 seconds. Add the tomatoes, dried fruits, and ¼ cup water, and bring to a simmer. Add the chicken back to the pot, skin side up, cover, and cook until it registers 160°F on a meat thermometer, 10 to 12 minutes more. Top with fresh parsley before serving.

NUTRITION (PER SERVING):

349 calories, **18 g protein**, 28 g carbohydrates, 4 g fiber, 17 g sugars, 19 g fat, 5 g saturated fat, 761 mg sodium

Spicy Chicken Chili

PREP TIME: 20 minutes **TOTAL TIME:** 1 hour 40 minutes Serves 8

1 ounce dried guajillo chiles (about 4), stems removed

2 cups boiling water

1 or 2 chipotle peppers in adobo, plus 1 to 2 tablespoons adobo sauce

1 large white onion, chopped

3 cloves garlic, smashed

1 can (4 ounces) diced green chiles

1 ½ pounds boneless skinless chicken thighs, cut into 1-inch pieces

2 teaspoons ground cumin

½ teaspoon ground cayenne

½ teaspoon kosher salt

½ teaspoon ground black pepper

3 tablespoons vegetable oil

1 quart low-sodium chicken broth

12 ounces lager-style beer

3 cans (14 ounces to 15 ounces) unsalted beans, such as kidney, black-eyed peas, and chickpeas, rinsed and drained

2 bunches Swiss chard, stems removed and leaves torn into bite-size pieces, about 10 cups

1. Place the dried chiles in medium bowl and cover with the water. Let steep until soft and pliable, about 15 minutes. Drain, reserving ½ cup liquid, and place in a blender with chipotle pepper, adobo sauce, onion, garlic, and green chiles. Blend until smooth and set aside.

2. Place the chicken in a large bowl and season with the cumin, cayenne, salt, and pepper, tossing well to coat. Heat the oil in a large Dutch oven or heavy pot over medium-high heat. Add the chicken and cook until browned, about 8 minutes. Remove the chicken with a slotted spoon and transfer to a plate.

3. Add the chile puree to the pot and cook until fragrant, about 1 minute. Add the broth, beer, beans, and chicken. Bring to a boil, reduce heat to medium-low, and simmer until the mixture thickens and the chicken becomes very tender, about 1 hour. In the last 10 minutes of cooking, stir in the chard, cooking until just tender. Serve with your favorite toppings.

NUTRITION (PER SERVING):

311 calories, **26 g protein**, 25 g carbohydrates, 7 g fiber, 2 g sugars, 11 g fat, 1.5 g saturated fat, 797 mg sodium

Peanut Broccoli and Chicken Salad with Soba Noodles

PREP TIME: 5 minutes **TOTAL TIME:** 25 minutes Serves 4

6 ounces (2 bundles) soba noodles

⅓ cup creamy peanut butter

2 tablespoons low-sodium soy sauce

1 tablespoon rice vinegar

2 teaspoons honey

1 teaspoon garlic powder

½ teaspoon ground ginger

4 trimmed boneless, skinless chicken thighs

1 tablespoon olive oil

1 head of broccoli, cut into florets

¼ cup peanuts, chopped

¼ cup cilantro, chopped

Kosher salt and black pepper to taste

1. Cook the soba noodles according to package directions. Reserve ½ cup noodle cooking water and drain the rest.

2. In a large bowl, whisk together the peanut butter, soy sauce, rice vinegar, and honey. Immediately coat the noodles in peanut sauce, adding the reserved cooking water to loosen the sauce.

3. Sprinkle the garlic powder and ginger evenly over both sides of the chicken thighs. Heat the olive oil in a large skillet over medium-high heat. Add the chicken to the skillet and cook, flipping once, until almost cooked through, 6 minutes. Add the broccoli. Cook, covered, until broccoli is bright green and crisp tender and chicken is cooked through, about 5 minutes more.

4. Coarsely chop the chicken and toss into the noodles with the broccoli. Top with peanuts and cilantro. Season to taste with salt and black pepper. Enjoy warm or at room temperature.

NUTRITION (PER SERVING):

504 calories, **32 g protein**, 52 g carbohydrates, 6 g fiber, 8 g sugar, 22 g fat, 4 g saturated fat, 877 mg sodium

Chicken and
Pineapple Kebaba

Chicken and Pineapple Kebabs

PREP TIME: 15 minutes **TOTAL TIME:** 1 hour Serves 4 (8 skewers)

1 lime, zested and juiced + wedges for serving

1 Serrano pepper, minced

¼ cup olive oil

½ cup chopped mint + leaves for serving

1½ teaspoons ground cumin

1 teaspoon kosher salt

¾ teaspoon ground black pepper

6 boneless, skinless chicken thighs, each cut into 4 equal pieces

½ fresh pineapple, peeled, cored and cut into 24 pieces

24 red or white pearl onions, trimmed and peeled

In a large bowl, combine lime zest, juice, Serrano, oil, mint, cumin, salt, and pepper. Stir well to mix. Add chicken, pineapple, and onions and marinate 20 minutes at room temperature. Thread the chicken, pineapple, and onions onto 8 skewers. Prepare a grill or heat a grill pan to medium-high heat. Grill kebabs until chicken is cooked through and onions soften, about 5 minutes per side. Serve topped with mint leaves and lime wedges.

NUTRITION (PER SERVING):

282 calories, **21 g protein**, 25 g carbohydrates, 2 g fiber, 14 g sugar, 11 g fat, 2 g saturated fat, 346 mg sodium

One Pan Chicken Tikki Dinner

One Pan Chicken Tikka Dinner

PREP TIME: 10 minutes **TOTAL TIME:** 55 minutes Serves 4

4 bone-in, skin-on chicken thighs

4 chicken drumsticks

1 cup jarred tikka masala sauce

4 cups cauliflower florets (from 1 medium head)

4 medium carrots, chopped

1 can (15 ounces) chickpeas, rinsed and drained

1 tablespoon olive oil

1 teaspoon garam masala

½ teaspoon kosher salt

½ teaspoon black pepper

½ medium red onion, thinly sliced

1 lemon, cut into 4 wedges

¼ cup plain low-fat yogurt

2 tablespoons chopped cilantro

1. In a bowl or zip top bag, combine chicken and tikka sauce, tossing to thoroughly coat. Let marinate at room temperature for at least 15 minutes or up to overnight in the refrigerator.

2. Heat the oven to 425°F. On a large rimmed baking sheet, toss together cauliflower, carrots, chickpeas, oil, garam masala, salt, and pepper. Remove chicken from marinade, discard excess marinade, and place the chicken throughout the pan. Roast until the vegetables are tender and chicken is cooked through (a thermometer inserted into the thickest part reads 165°F), about 30 minutes.

3. Meanwhile, place onion in a bowl with enough water to cover. Serve the chicken with the drained onion, lemon, yogurt, and cilantro.

NUTRITION (PER SERVING):

472 calories, **46 g protein**, 37 g carbohydrates, 10 g fiber, 11 g sugars, 16 g fat, 4 g saturated fat, 635 mg sodium

Skillet-Sizzled Chicken Wings

PREP TIME: 5 minutes **TOTAL TIME:** 30 minutes Serves 4

1½ pounds chicken wings

1 tablespoon vegetable oil

½ teaspoon kosher salt

½ teaspoon ground black pepper

2 tablespoons butter, melted

1 tablespoon hot sauce, more to taste

2 celery ribs, cut into 2-inch lengths

1. Heat the oven to 500°F. In a large bowl, toss the chicken wings with the oil, salt, and black pepper until well coated.

2. In a large cast-iron skillet, place the wings skin side down leaving some space around each one. Slide the skillet into the oven and roast for 10 minutes. Flip the wings and continue to roast until cooked through, 10 minutes more. Turn the broiler on high and broil the wings until crisp, 5 minutes more.

3. Meanwhile, mix your butter and hot sauce in a large bowl. Remove your wings from the oven and toss in the bowl with the hot sauce and butter mix and transfer to a plate. Serve with celery sticks.

NUTRITION (PER SERVING):

354 calories, **23 g protein**, 1 g carbs, 0 g fiber, 0 g sugar, 29 g fat, 9.5 g saturated fat, 473 mg sodium

Healthier Hot Wings

Healthier Hot Wings

PREP TIME: 10 minutes **TOTAL TIME:** 45 minutes Serves 4

2 pounds chicken wings, separated

¾ cup plain Greek yogurt

3 tablespoons grated Parmesan cheese

3 teaspoons Dijon mustard, divided

½ teaspoon ground black pepper

1 cup buffalo hot sauce

1 tablespoon honey

Celery stalks, cucumber spears, or radishes (for serving)

1. Heat the oven to 500°F and lightly coat a large rimmed baking sheet with a rack with cooking spray.

2. Place a steamer basket inside of a large pot with 1 inch of water. Bring to a simmer over medium-high heat. Add chicken to the steamer basket, cover and cook for 10 minutes.

3. Meanwhile, in a small bowl, stir together yogurt, cheese, 1 teaspoon Dijon mustard, and pepper.

4. Remove the wings from the steamer basket and arrange on the sheet pan. Roast until golden brown and crisp, about 25 minutes. Meanwhile, whisk together buffalo sauce, honey, and remaining mustard in a large bowl. Toss the wings in the buffalo sauce and serve with Parmesan yogurt dip and vegetables.

NUTRITION (PER SERVING):

260 calories, **24 g protein**, 4 g carbohydrates, 0 g fiber, 3 g sugars, 16 g fat, 5.5 g saturated fat, 547 mg sodium

BORED OF BUFFALO WINGS?

Just replace the hot sauce in the recipe above with these flavor changers. Then try them with the fresh-tasting options below to bust out of a celery-and-blue-cheese rut.

Jalapeño Honey Mustard

¼ cup honey mustard

2 teaspoons pickled jalapeño juice

Serve with: chilled halved radishes

NUTRITION (PER SERVING): 388 CALORIES, 23 G PROTEIN, 8 G CARBOHYDRATES, 1 G FIBER, 5 G SUGAR, 30 G FAT, 9.5 G SATURATED FAT, 515 MG SODIUM

Chipotle Pineapple

3 tablespoons chopped chipotles in adobo sauce

3 tablespoons crushed pineapple in juice

2 tablespoons pineapple juice

Serve with: grilled scallions

NUTRITION (PER SERVING): 368 CALORIES, 23 G PROTEIN, 3 G CARBOHYDRATES, 0 G FIBER, 2 G SUGAR, 29 G FAT, 9.5 G SATURATED FAT, 415 MG SODIUM

Citrus Sweet Chili

¼ cup Thai sweet chili sauce

2 tablespoons lime juice

1 teaspoon orange zest

Serve with: avocado wedges

NUTRITION (PER SERVING): 386 CALORIES, 23 G PROTEIN, 7 G CARBOHYDRATES, 0 G FIBER, 6 G SUGAR, 29 G FAT, 9.5 G SATURATED FAT, 500 MG SODIUM

Chicken Thigh Saltimbocca

PREP TIME: 5 minutes **TOTAL TIME:** 30 minutes Serves 2

1 tablespoon olive oil

2 boneless, skinless chicken thighs

2 fresh sage leaves

2 slices fresh mozzarella

2 slices prosciutto

1. Heat oven to 400°F. Heat an oven-safe skillet over medium and coat with olive oil.

2. On top of a chicken thigh, place a fresh sage leaf and a slice of fresh mozzarella. Wrap a slice of prosciutto around everything to form a bundle and secure with a toothpick. Repeat with the second thigh.

3. Sear the chicken in the skillet, 2 minutes. Place the skillet in the oven and cook until an instant-read thermometer reads 165°F, 20 to 30 minutes.

NUTRITION (PER SERVING):
276 calories, **25 g protein**, 2 g carbohydrates, 0 g fiber, 0 g sugars, 19 g fat, 7 g saturated fat, 650 mg sodium

Asian Cold Noodle Bowl

PREP TIME: 15 minutes **TOTAL TIME:** 25 minutes Serves 4

12 ounces whole wheat spaghetti

3 boneless, skinless chicken thighs, thinly sliced

½ cup chunky peanut butter

⅓ cup low-sodium soy sauce

4 cloves garlic

2 tablespoons red wine vinegar

1 tablespoon brown sugar

2 teaspoons toasted sesame oil

1 small cucumber, seeded and chopped

½ cup shredded carrots

Scallion, red pepper flakes, peanuts (for garnish)

1. Cook the spaghetti according to package directions. Rinse under cold water to cool, and set aside.

2. Spray a wok or skillet with cooking spray and heat over medium-high. Add the chicken and cook until no longer pink, 8 minutes. Transfer the chicken to a plate and refrigerate.

3. Meanwhile, stir together the peanut butter, soy sauce, garlic, vinegar, brown sugar, and sesame oil.

4. In a serving bowl, toss together the spaghetti, chicken, cucumber, carrots, and the sauce until completely coated. Garnish with thinly sliced scallion, a pinch of red pepper flakes, and chopped peanuts, if desired.

NUTRITION (PER SERVING):
592 calories, **32 g protein**, 79 g carbohydrates, 14 g fiber, 10 g sugars, 20 g fat, 3.5 g saturated fat, 932 mg sodium

Easy Burritos

PREP TIME: 10 minutes **TOTAL TIME:** 25 minutes Serves 4

4 boneless, skinless chicken thighs, sliced

2 tablespoons chili powder

1 tablespoon cumin

½ teaspoon kosher salt

1 tablespoon olive oil

1 cup crushed tomatoes

1 teaspoon chopped fresh oregano

4 10-inch whole wheat tortillas

1 cup chopped lettuce

1 avocado, sliced

4 tablespoons Cheddar cheese

4 teaspoons hot sauce

1. In a bowl, toss the chicken with chili powder, cumin, and salt.

2. Warm the olive oil in a large skillet over medium heat. Add the chicken and cook, stirring, until browned, about 8 minutes. Add the tomatoes and oregano and simmer until the chicken is tender, 10 to 15 minutes.

3. Divide the chicken among the tortillas and roll up with the lettuce, avocado, cheese, and hot sauce.

NUTRITION (PER SERVING):

310 calories, **21 g protein**, 31 g carbohydrates, 7 g fiber, 3 g sugars, 15 g fat, 3.5 g saturated fat, 793 mg sodium

Grilled Spice-Rubbed Chicken with Peaches

PREP TIME: 10 minutes **TOTAL TIME:** 30 minutes Serves 4

Vegetable or canola oil for the grill

2 tablespoons whole cumin seeds, toasted and ground or 1 tablespoon ground cumin

2 tablespoons brown sugar

2 tablespoons smoked paprika

1 teaspoon kosher salt

½ teaspoon freshly ground black pepper

4 bone in skin on chicken thighs

4 bone in skin on chicken drumsticks

4 ripe peaches

1. Prepare a grill for indirect grilling over medium-high heat. Brush and oil the grates.

2. Combine cumin, brown sugar, paprika, salt and pepper, and rub all over chicken. Place chicken over direct heat and cook 2 to 3 minutes per side. Move the chicken to indirect heat and cook, rotating occasionally, until internal temperature reaches 165°F, about 18 minutes.

3. Meanwhile, halve the peaches and remove the pits. Brush lightly with oil and grill, cut side down, until charred and softened, 5 minutes. Serve the chicken and peaches together.

NUTRITION (PER SERVING):

426 calories, **53 g protein**, 25 g carbohydrates, 4 g fiber, 19 g sugars, 13 g fat, 3 g saturated fat, 745 mg sodium

The Ultimate Roasted Whole Chicken

THE WHOLE BIRD

The Ultimate Roasted Whole Chicken

PREP TIME: 5 minutes **TOTAL TIME:** 1 hour 15 minutes Serves 4

1 whole chicken (3 to 4 pounds)

½ lemon

1 tablespoon kosher salt

1. About an hour before cooking, take the chicken out of the refrigerator.

2. Heat the oven to 450°F. Stuff the lemon half in the cavity of the chicken and place in an oven-safe skillet. Sprinkle the kosher salt all over the chicken and bake until a thermometer inserted in the thigh reads 165°F, 1 to 1¼ hours. Remove from oven and rest for 15 minutes before slicing.

NUTRITION (PER SERVING):
483 calories, **42 g protein**, 0 g carbohydrates, 0 g fiber, 0 g sugars, 34 g fat, 10 g saturated fat, 1117 mg sodium

Note: Want a quick sauce for plain roasted chicken? While the bird rests, bring the juices and fat in the skillet to a boil, and add ½ cup white wine or water, using a flat-edged wooden spoon to scrape the browned bits on the bottom of the skillet. To finish, stir in a tablespoon of Dijon mustard and spoon over the sliced chicken.

EASY CHICKEN SEASONINGS

Jerk Seasoning

Combine 2 tablespoons of jerk seasoning with 1 tablespoon olive oil until it forms a paste. Coat the chicken with the jerk paste before roasting. Serve chicken with black beans and rice.

NUTRITION (PER SERVING): 30 CALORIES, 0 G PROTEIN, 0 G CARBOHYDRATES, 0 G FIBER, 0 G SUGARS, 3.5 G FAT, 0.5 G SATURATED FAT, 420 MG SODIUM

Honey Citrus

Mix 1 tablespoon fresh orange juice, 1 tablespoon honey, 1 tablespoon Dijon mustard, and 1½ teaspoons soy sauce. Carefully loosen the skin of the chicken with your fingers and rub the sauce all over the chicken underneath the skin.

NUTRITION (PER SERVING): 22 CALORIES, 0 G PROTEIN, 6 G CARBOHYDRATES, 0 G FIBER, 5 G SUGARS, 0 G FAT, 0 G SATURATED FAT, 200 MG SODIUM

Chimichurri

While the bird roasts, mix together 1 cup of freshly chopped leafy herbs and/or spicy greens (parsley, chives, mint, cilantro , arugula, watercress) with 1 clove minced garlic, 2 minced anchovies, 1 tablespoon capers (drained and chopped), 1 tablespoon fresh lemon juice, a pinch of kosher salt and black pepper, and 3 tablespoons good olive oil. Serve over the cut chicken. Makes ½ cup (serves 4).

NUTRITION (PER SERVING): 100 CALORIES, 1 G PROTEIN, 1 G CARBOHYDRATES, 0 G FIBER, 0 G SUGARS, 10 G FAT, 1.5 G SATURATED FAT, 198 MG SODIUM

Asian BBQ

Make a quick Asian BBQ sauce to serve with the cooked chicken: combine of ½ cup ketchup, ¼ cup low-sodium soy sauce, 2 tablespoons brown sugar, 2 cloves minced garlic, and 2 teaspoons ground ginger. Makes ¾ cup (serves 4).

NUTRITION (PER SERVING): 80 CALORIES, 2 G PROTEIN, 18 G CARBOHYDRATES, 0 G FIBER, 14 G SUGARS, 0 G FAT, 0 G SATURATED FAT, 886 MG SODIUM

Blackened Matcha Spice Rub

Combine 4 teaspoons matcha powder, 2 teaspoons each ground black pepper and garlic powder, 1 teaspoon each kosher salt, ground ginger, ground mustard (mustard powder), ground thyme, and ½ teaspoon each cayenne pepper and paprika. Rub half of this spice mixture under the skin of the chicken before roasting. Store the remaining half in an airtight container for up to 6 months.

NUTRITION (PER SERVING): 28 CALORIES, 1 G PROTEIN, 5 G CARBOHYDRATES, 1 G FIBER, 2 G SUGAR, 0 G FAT, 0 G SATURATED FAT, 490 MG SODIUM

Sunday's Choose-Your-Own-Adventure Chicken Soup

PREP TIME: 20 minutes **TOTAL TIME:** 4 hours 40 minutes Serves 8

For the stock:

1 leftover chicken carcass (for example, from Rosemary Garlic Chicken, page 85)

1 small onion, coarsely chopped

1 medium carrot, coarsely chopped

1 celery stalk, coarsely chopped

½ bunch parsley, rinsed

1 bay leaf

1 teaspoon whole black peppercorns

For the soup:

1 teaspoon olive oil

2 celery stalks, diced

2 medium carrots, diced

1 small onion, diced

2 cups chopped kale

1 can (15 ounces) white beans, drained and rinsed

2 cups leftover chicken (light and/or dark meat), chopped or shredded

1 teaspoon kosher salt

½ teaspoon ground black pepper

Grated Parmesan cheese, for topping

For the stock:

Combine the chicken carcass, onion, carrot, celery, parsley, bay leaf, and peppercorns in a large slow cooker. Add enough water to cover (about 8 cups). Cook on high 4 hours or on low 8 hours and up to overnight. Strain the stock and discard the solids. You can either use immediately or cool the stock completely and refrigerate up to 1 week or freeze for up to 3 months.

For the soup:

In a large pot over medium heat, warm the oil. Add the celery, carrot, and onion and cook until softened, about 5 minutes. Add the reserved stock, kale (or your extra vegetable options on page 84), beans (or your starchy addition on page 84), chicken, salt, and pepper and bring to a simmer. Cook until the vegetables and/or pasta are tender, about 10 minutes. Season to taste with salt and pepper and serve with Parmesan (or your choice of toppings).

Note: Save that chicken carcass! This is a great soup for using up whatever veggies you might have in your crisper and pastas or garnishes that might be lurking in your cupboards. Check out the options we created following this recipe.

NUTRITION (PER SERVING):

217 calories, **21 g protein**, 21 g carbohydrates, 3 g fiber, 5 g sugar, 5 g fat, 1 g saturated fat, 636 mg sodium

PERSONALIZE YOUR SOUP

Up your adventure by selecting any of these terrific options for your soup.

Extra Vegetable Options (pick 1 or 2):

2 cups chopped leafy greens (such as kale, spinach, chard)

2 cups green beans, chopped

2 cups green peas

2 cups diced butternut squash

Starchy additions (pick 1):

½ cup orzo or ditalini pasta

2 medium potatoes, peeled and diced

1 large sweet potato, peeled and diced

1 can (15 ounces) beans (any type), drained and rinsed

Optional Toppings:

Shredded Parmesan cheese

French fried onions (such as French's)

Thinly sliced scallions

Toasted pumpkin seeds

Dollops of leftover Boozy Gravy (page 85)

A spoon of cranberry sauce

Croutons made of leftover stuffing or bread

Squeeze of fresh lemon juice

Rosemary Garlic Chicken with Boozy Gravy

PREP TIME: 10 minutes **TOTAL TIME:** 1 hour 15 minutes Serves 4

For the bird:

2 tablespoons unsalted butter, softened

1 tablespoon chopped fresh rosemary

1 clove garlic, mashed with a chef's knife

½ teaspoon kosher salt, divided

½ teaspoon ground black pepper, divided

1 whole chicken (3 to 4 pounds), separated into drumsticks, thighs, and breasts

For the gravy:

¼ cup booze of choice (beer, white or red wine, bourbon)

1 cup low-sodium chicken broth

1 tablespoon unsalted butter, softened

1 tablespoon all-purpose flour

¼ teaspoon kosher salt, or to taste

¼ teaspoon ground black pepper, or to taste

1. Heat the oven to 425°F. Set a flat rack on a rimmed baking sheet and set aside.

2. Combine the butter, rosemary, garlic, and ¼ teaspoon each salt and pepper in a small bowl and set aside.

3. Rub the butter mixture under the skin and all over the chicken parts. Transfer to the prepared baking sheet and season with the remaining salt and pepper. Pour a cup of water into the bottom of the baking sheet and roast the chicken for 20 minutes. Reduce the heat to 350°F and continue to roast until an instant-read thermometer inserted in the thickest part of the meat, while not touching bone, registers 160°F (carry over cooking will take it the rest of the way to 165°F), about 20 minutes. Transfer the cooked chicken to a cutting board and tent with foil for 15 minutes. Meanwhile, make your gravy.

4. Pour your chicken drippings into a measuring cup and let sit for 5 minutes to separate the fat. Pour the booze into the baking sheet and use it to scrape up any remaining browned bits with a wooden spoon. Strain it into a small saucepan. Remove and discard as much fat as you can from the drippings and then pour the remaining drippings into the saucepan along with the broth. Bring to a boil over high heat and reduce by half, about 15 minutes. Combine the butter and flour to form a paste. Whisk in small amounts of the butter-flour mixture until the gravy is the thickness you desire. Season to taste with salt and pepper. Pour directly over chicken or into a gravy boat.

NUTRITION (PER SERVING, CHICKEN ONLY):
246 calories, **35 g protein**, 1 g carbohydrates, 0 g fiber, 0g sugar, 10 g fat, 5 g saturated fat, 371mg sodium

NUTRITION (PER SERVING, GRAVY ONLY, 2 TBSP.):
78 calories, **1 g protein**, 2 g carbohydrates, 0 g fiber, 0 g sugar, 6 g fat, 3 g saturated fat, 139 mg sodium

Grill-Roasted Chicken with Lime Butter and Green Beans

PREP TIME: 5 minutes **TOTAL TIME:** 1 hour Serves 6

- **1½ tablespoons fresh lime juice**
- **2 tablespoons butter**
- **1 small shallot, minced**
- **½ teaspoon Dijon mustard**
- **1 whole chicken (3 to 4 pounds), butterflied (see Note)**
- **1 teaspoon kosher salt, divided**
- **1 pound green beans, trimmed**
- **1 tablespoon olive oil**
- **¼ teaspoon ground black pepper**
- **1 tablespoon minced parsley**

1. Prepare a grill for indirect cooking with your hot zone on high. Brush and oil the grates. Place a small saucepan over direct heat and bring the lime juice to a simmer. Add the butter and swirl the pan over the heat until the butter is completely melted. Remove from the heat and swirl in the minced shallot and mustard; leave off heat.

2. Close the lid and let the grill get very hot, about 5 minutes. Season the chicken with ½ teaspoon salt and transfer it breast side down on the hot zone. Close the lid, and cook until the skin is crisped, about 10 minutes. Flip the bird and move it to the cool side of the grill. Close the lid, and cook, basting with the lime sauce, about every 6 minutes, or 3 times total, until the chicken breast reaches 165°F, about 20 minutes more. Transfer to a cutting board to rest.

3. Toss the beans with the olive oil, remaining salt and black pepper. Put them in a grill basket and put over direct heat. Cover the grill, but toss the beans frequently so that they cook evenly, about 10 minutes.

4. Slice the chicken into 8 pieces (2 wings, 2 breast halves, 2 thighs, 2 drumsticks) and serve with the green beans, topped with the parsley.

NUTRITION (PER SERVING):
464 calories, **34 g protein**, 8 g carbs, 2 g fiber, 3 g sugar, 33 g fat, 10.5 g saturated fat, 331 mg sodium

Note: To butterfly or spatchcock the chicken: Put the chicken on a cutting board, breast side down. Using poultry shears, cut along both sides of the backbone; remove and discard the backbone. Flip the chicken over and press down gently to break the breastbone and flatten the breast slightly. The butcher at the supermarket can also do it for you.

Grill-Roasted Chicken
with Lime Butter and Green Beans

Roasted Dry-Brine Chicken and Vegetables

PREP TIME: 5 minutes **TOTAL TIME:** 1 hour 30 minutes plus brining time Serves 4

1 whole chicken (3 to 4 pounds)

2 teaspoons kosher salt

1 pound baby potatoes, halved

1 pound Brussels sprouts, halved

1 pound carrots, peeled and cut into 1-inch chunks

2 large shallots, cut into wedges

2 tablespoons olive oil, divided

Kosher salt and ground black pepper

1. The day before cooking, place the chicken on a plate and rub the salt all over. Set in the refrigerator, uncovered, and let rest overnight. The skin will darken overnight, don't worry that's natural.

2. Heat the oven to 450°F. In a large oven-safe skillet, toss together the potatoes, Brussels sprouts, carrots, shallots, 1 tablespoon oil, and a sprinkle of salt and pepper.

3. Remove the chicken from the refrigerator and rinse under cold water. Pat dry and rub all over with the remaining tablespoon oil and season generously with pepper. Place on top of the vegetables and roast until an instant read thermometer registers 165°F in the thickest part of the breast and the vegetables are all tender, about 1½ hours.

4. Remove the pan from the oven and transfer the chicken to a cutting board. With a large spoon toss the vegetables to coat them in the pan drippings. Serve the chicken with the vegetables.

NUTRITION (PER SERVING):
394 calories, **33 g protein**, 46 g carbohydrates, 9 g fiber, 11 g sugar, 11 g fat, 2 g saturated fat, 696 mg sodium

Miso-Rubbed Chicken with Acorn Squash

PREP TIME: 15 minutes **TOTAL TIME:** 1 hour 30 minutes Serves 6

¼ cup white (shiro) miso

2 scallions, coarsely chopped

1 two-inch piece ginger, peeled and coarsely chopped

1 tablespoon honey

2 teaspoon low sodium soy sauce

1 large (2½ to 3 pounds) acorn squash, seeded and cut into ½-inch-thick wedges

1 Thai chile pepper, sliced (optional)

1 tablespoon vegetable oil

1 whole chicken (3 to 4 pounds)

1. Heat the oven to 425°F and lightly spray a large rimmed baking sheet with cooking spray.

2. In a food processor, combine the miso, scallions, ginger, honey, and soy sauce and process until smooth. In a large bowl, toss the acorn squash, chile pepper, if using, and oil to coat.

3. Place the chicken on the prepared baking sheet and with your fingers gently separate the skin from the meat, taking care not to tear the skin. Spread the miso mixture on the meat and all over the skin. Scatter squash pieces around the chicken and roast for 20 minutes.

4. Reduce the heat to 375°F and continue roasting until chicken is golden, a meat thermometer registers 160°F when inserted into the thigh, and the squash is tender, 25 to 30 minutes more. Let the chicken rest 20 minutes before carving.

NUTRITION (PER SERVING):
460 calories, **34 g protein**, 15 g carbohydrates, 1 g fiber, 7 g sugars, 29 g fat, 8 g saturated fat, 498 mg sodium

Cherry Wood–Smoked Pulled Chicken

PREP TIME: 10 minutes **TOTAL TIME:** 1 hour 20 minutes plus marinating time Serves 6

1½ cups plain whole milk yogurt

3 cloves garlic, mashed to a paste

1 tablespoon fresh lemon juice

1 teaspoon kosher salt

1 teaspoon ground black pepper

½ teaspoon smoked paprika

½ teaspoon cumin

1 whole chicken (3 to 4 pounds), spatch-cocked or butterflied, see note page 86

1 cup cherry wood chips (soaked in water for 30 minutes if using a charcoal grill)

Canola oil for the grill

1 cup barbecue sauce (see sidebar page 91)

1. In a large zip-top bag, add the yogurt, garlic, lemon juice, salt, pepper, paprika, and cumin; seal and squeeze the bag to combine. Add the chicken and reseal the top; agitate the bag and gently squeeze, making sure to completely coat the chicken. Place it in a bowl and refrigerate it 8 hours and up to overnight.

2. Prepare a gas or charcoal grill for indirect cooking with medium heat: On a gas grill, heat all burners on high; then turn off all but one or two burners to maintain a temperature of 300°F. Use two layers of heavy-duty aluminum foil to make a V-shaped packet to hold the wood chips. Set the packet between the active burners. Sprinkle the dry chips into the packet. On a charcoal grill, light your charcoal and bank the coals to one side on the grill, leaving the other half with no direct heat source; sprinkle the soaked chips over the coals. Brush and oil the grilling grates.

3. Place the chicken on the hot side of the grill, skin side down, and grill until grill marks form, about 4 minutes. Flip, transfer to the cool side, skin side up, and grill, covered, rotating occasionally, until an instant-read thermometer inserted in the thickest part of the breast registers 165°F and the thickest part of the thigh registers 175°F, about 45 minutes.

4. Transfer to a cutting board and let rest 10 minutes. Remove and discard the skin. Pick the chicken clean and shred the meat.

5. Warm 1 cup of your favorite BBQ sauce in a large skillet, and add the shredded chicken. Cook over medium heat, stirring, until the chicken is completely coated in sauce and heated through.

6. Serve in a bun, on lettuce leaves, or on its own.

NUTRITION (PER SERVING):
263 calories, **32 g protein**, 20 g carbohydrates, 1 g fiber, 16 g sugars, 5 g fat, 1.5 g saturated fat, 682 mg sodium

4 TANGY BBQ SAUCES

Yellow BBQ Sauce

In a small saucepan over medium heat, combine ½ cup prepared yellow mustard, ¼ cup plus 2 tablespoons honey, 2 teaspoons Worcestershire sauce, 1 teaspoon each garlic powder and onion powder, and ¼ teaspoon smoked paprika. Whisk until smooth. Makes about 1 cup.

NUTRITION (PER SERVING): 82 CALORIES, 1 G PROTEIN, 19 G CARBOHYDRATES, 1 G FIBER, 18 G SUGARS, 1 G FAT, 0 G SATURATED FAT, 247 MG SODIUM

Vinegary BBQ Sauce

In a small bowl, whisk together ¾ cup white vinegar, 2 tablespoons hot sauce (such as Frank's Red Hot), 2 tablespoons tomato paste, 1 tablespoon maple syrup, 1 teaspoon molasses, and 1 teaspoon crushed red pepper flakes until smooth. For optimal flavor, store in the refrigerator overnight before using. Makes about 1 cup.

NUTRITION (PER SERVING): 18 CALORIES, 0 G PROTEIN, 4 G CARBOHYDRATES, 0 G FIBER, 4 G SUGARS, 0 G FAT, 0 G SATURATED FAT, 168 MG SODIUM

Spicy BBQ Sauce

Heat 1 teaspoon olive oil in a medium saucepan over medium-high heat. Add 1 clove minced garlic, ½ jalapeno (seeded and chopped), and 2 tablespoons minced onion and cook until softened, 3 to 4 minutes. Stir in ¼ teaspoon each Ancho chili powder and cayenne, and cook for 1 minute more. Add 1 cup chili sauce (such as Heinz) and cook until heated through, about 5 minutes. Carefully transfer to a blender and blend until smooth. Season to taste with kosher salt and black pepper. Makes about 1 cup.

NUTRITION (PER SERVING): 57 CALORIES, 1 G PROTEIN, 10 G CARBOHYDRATES, 3 G FIBER, 5 G SUGARS, 1 G FAT, 0 G SATURATED FAT, 629 MG SODIUM

Sweet Plum BBQ Sauce

In a medium saucepan over medium heat, cook 2 or 3 ripe plums (pitted and chopped), 2 or 3 plum tomatoes (seeded and chopped), ¼ cup chopped red onion, 1 crushed clove garlic, 1 star anise, ½ cinnamon stick, 2 whole cloves, and 2 tablespoons water until soft, 10 to 15 minutes. Strain to remove skins and spices, and transfer back to the saucepan. Stir in ¼ cup currants, 2 tablespoons brown sugar, 1 tablespoon tomato paste, 1 teaspoon chili powder, and ½ teaspoon kosher salt and cook until the sugar is dissolved, 1 to 2 minutes. Stir in 1 teaspoon red wine vinegar; season to taste with salt and sugar. Makes about 1 cup.

NUTRITION (PER SERVING): 57 CALORIES, 1 G PROTEIN, 14 G CARBOHYDRATES, 1 G FIBER, 12 G SUGARS, 0 G FAT, 0 G SATURATED FAT, 185 MG SODIUM

Rosemary, Orange, and Fennel Spatchcocked Chicken

PREP TIME: 10 minutes **TOTAL TIME:** 55 minutes Serves 6

1 whole chicken (3 to 4 pounds), spatchcocked or butterflied, see note page 86

2 teaspoons olive oil

2 tablespoons fresh orange zest

1 tablespoons chopped fresh rosemary

2 teaspoons fennel seeds, toasted and crushed

½ teaspoon kosher salt

¼ to ½ teaspoon crushed red pepper flakes

1. Heat the oven to 375°F and lightly spray a large rimmed baking sheet with cooking spray.

2. Rub the chicken with oil. In a small bowl, stir together the orange zest, rosemary, fennel seeds, salt, and red pepper and rub over chicken.

3. Transfer the chicken to the prepared baking sheet and roast until a meat thermometer registers 160°F when inserted into the thigh, about 45 minutes. Let the chicken rest for 20 minutes before carving.

NUTRITION (PER SERVING):

147 calories, **24 g protein**, 1 g carbohydrates, 1 g fiber, 0 g sugars, 5 g fat, 1 g saturated fat, 248 mg sodium

Herb-Roasted Chicken with Potatoes and Brussels Sprouts

PREP TIME: 20 minutes **TOTAL TIME:** 1 hour 40 minutes Serves 6

½ pound baby Yukon gold potatoes

½ pound small carrots with tops

2 tablespoons olive oil, divided

1 whole chicken (3 to 4 pounds)

¼ cup chopped fresh parsley

2 tablespoons chopped fresh thyme leaves

4 teaspoons grated lemon zest

1 teaspoon kosher salt

1 teaspoon black pepper

1 pound Brussels sprouts, trimmed and large ones halved

½ loaf whole wheat baguette, cut into 1-inch cubes (about 2 cups)

1. Heat the oven to 450°F. Spray a large rimmed baking sheet with cooking spray.

2. Add the potatoes, carrots and 1½ teaspoons of the oil, and toss to coat. Add the chicken and drizzle with 1½ teaspoons oil. Sprinkle the chicken and vegetables with the parsley, thyme, lemon zest, salt, and pepper. Roast for 20 minutes; reduce the heat to 375°F.

3. In a large bowl, toss together the Brussels sprouts and bread with the remaining 1 tablespoon oil. Add to the baking sheet, and roast until the chicken registers 165°F on a meat thermometer, about 40 minutes. Rest the chicken 15 minutes before serving with the vegetables and croutons.

NUTRITION (PER SERVING):

478 calories, **33 g protein**, 26 g carbohydrates, 5 g fiber, 4 g sugar, 27 g fat, 7 g saturated fat, 576 mg sodium

Braised Chicken with Bacon and Green Olives

PREP TIME: 10 minutes plus resting time **TOTAL TIME:** 1 hour 20 minutes Serves 6

1 whole chicken (3 to 4 pounds), separated into legs, wings, and breasts

Kosher salt and ground black pepper

2 slices bacon, chopped

2 tablespoons all-purpose flour

2 teaspoons olive oil

10 large shallots, peeled and halved

1 cup dry white vermouth

1 bunch (½ ounce) fresh thyme, tied with string

3 cups low-sodium chicken broth

12 green olives, such as Lucques or Picholine, pitted

1. Season the chicken with salt and pepper and let sit at room temperature for 1 to 2 hours.

2. Heat the oven to 300°F. In an 8-quart Dutch oven over medium heat, cook the bacon until crisp and the fat is rendered, about 10 minutes. Using a slotted spoon, transfer the bacon to a plate.

3. Meanwhile, dredge the chicken pieces in flour, shaking off the excess. Sear the chicken in the bacon fat in batches, adding olive oil if the pan gets too dry, about 6 minutes per side. Remove to the plate with the bacon.

4. Brown the shallots in the fat, 2 to 3 minutes. Add the vermouth, thyme, chicken legs, bacon, collected juices, and enough broth to go up about two thirds of the way up the side of the meat. Bring to a boil, reduce to a simmer and cook, uncovered, for 15 minutes. Add the chicken breasts, cover, and transfer to the oven. Cook until the meat is cooked through and tender, about 30 minutes. Remove the thyme bundle, stir in the olives and serve.

NUTRITION (PER SERVING):
544 calories, **36 g protein**, 27 g carbohydrates, 0 g fiber, 5 g sugars, 29 g fat, 8.5 g saturated fat, 556 mg sodium

Poached Chicken de Lima

PREP TIME: 10 minutes plus resting time **TOTAL TIME:** 2 hours Serves 8

2 whole chickens (3 to 4 pounds each)

Kosher salt and ground black pepper

8 cups low-sodium chicken broth

6 bay leaves

1 tablespoon dried Mexican oregano

1 cinnamon stick

5 garlic cloves

Zest of 1 grapefruit in strips

3 leeks, halved lengthwise, cleaned and cut into 2-inch pieces

2 ribs celery, cut into 1-inch pieces

2 carrots, peeled and cut into 1-inch chunks

3 chayote squash, scrubbed and cut into 1-inch chunks

6 fingerling potatoes, scrubbed and cut into 1-inch chunks

3 roma tomatoes, cored and cut into ¾-inch pieces

⅓ cup fresh lime juice (from 2 or 3 medium)

Garnishes:

3 red hot chiles, washed, stemmed and sliced into thin rounds

1 Hass avocado, firm ripe, cut into ¾-inch dice

1 cup baked tortilla chips, crushed

1 to 2 cups coarsely chopped fresh cilantro (from 1 large bunch)

2 limes, cut into wedges

1. Pat the chickens dry and season liberally, inside and out, with salt and pepper. Let sit at room temperature for 1 to 2 hours.

2. Place the chickens, broth, and enough water to cover in a large stockpot. Add the bay leaves, oregano, cinnamon, garlic, and grapefruit zest and bring to a boil. Cover and reduce heat to a gentle simmer and cook for 1 hour.

3. Add the leeks, celery, carrots, chayote and potatoes and gently simmer for 20 minutes. Remove from heat and let stand for 15 minutes.

4. Transfer the chicken and vegetables to a large serving platter and cover with aluminum foil to keep warm. Discard the bay leaves, cinnamon, garlic and grapefruit zest. Bring the broth to a boil, add the tomatoes and lime juice, season to taste with salt.

5. Carve the chickens, discarding the skin, and serve in shallow bowls with the vegetables and plenty of seasoned broth. Pass the garnishes for guests to add to their individual bowls.

NUTRITION (PER SERVING):
463 calories, **46 g protein**, 47 g carbs, 9 g fiber, 6 g sugars, 12 g fat, 2.5 g saturated fat, 408 mg sodium

Giblet Gravy

PREP TIME: 5 minutes **TOTAL TIME:** 3½ hours Serves 6 (Makes about 2½ cups)

½ pound chicken giblets, neck, and tail

1 onion, unpeeled, cut into wedges

2 carrots, coarsely chopped (no need to peel)

1 rib celery, coarsely chopped

1 tablespoon olive oil

6 cups water

Handful of parsley stems

2 sprigs thyme

1 bay leaf

½ teaspoon black peppercorns

3 tablespoons chicken fat, optional

2 tablespoons unsalted butter, softened

2 tablespoons all-purpose flour

1. Heat the oven to 400°F. Toss the giblets and bones, onion, carrots, celery, and oil in a small roasting pan. Roast, tossing occasionally, until everything is well browned, about 1 hour.

2. Transfer the bones and vegetables to a 3-quart saucepan. Add 1 cup of the water to the roasting pan and scrape off all the brown bits with a wooden spoon; transfer back to the saucepan and cover with an additional 5 cups water. Add the parsley stems, thyme, bay leaf, and peppercorns and bring to a bare simmer. Cook until the stock is flavorful and rich, about 2 hours. Strain stock into a smaller saucepan and set aside. You should have about 1¾ cups. Discard the solids. If roasting a chicken along side this gravy, add the chicken fat, if desired.

3. In a small bowl, using a spoon or your fingers, knead the butter and flour together. Bring the stock to a boil, and whisk in the butter mixture by tablespoonfuls until the desired thickness is reached. Allow the gravy to simmer for a minute before adding more. Season to taste with salt and pepper. Serve in a warm gravy boat alongside the chicken or over vegetables.

NUTRITION (PER SERVING):

69 calories, **2 g protein**, 5 g carbohydrates, 0 g fiber, 1 g sugars, 5 g fat, 3 g saturated fat, 101 mg sodium

Roast Chicken with Grape Sauce

PREP TIME: 10 minutes **TOTAL TIME:** 1 hour, 10 minutes plus resting time Serves 4

2 tablespoons unsalted butter

½ cup minced shallot (from 3 medium)

1 cup red wine, divided

2 cups low-sodium chicken broth

2 tablespoons honey

2 tablespoons sherry vinegar

1 tablespoons cornstarch dissolved in ¼ cup water

Kosher salt and freshly ground black pepper

1 whole chicken (3 to 4 pounds)

1 bay leaf

1 celery stalk, cut in thirds

½ pound fresh seedless red or black grapes, halved

½ pound fresh seedless green grapes, halved

½ cup pecans, lightly roasted, coarsely chopped

1. Melt 1 tablespoon butter in a 3-quart saucepan over low heat. Cook the shallots until soft and golden, about 10 minutes. Increase heat to high, add ½ cup of the wine and reduce by one-third. Add the chicken broth and reduce by one third. Add the honey and sherry vinegar, season to taste with salt and pepper. Whisk cornstarch mixture into the sauce and simmer until slightly thickened, 3 to 4 minutes. Set aside.

2. Heat the oven to 425°F. Season the chicken's cavity with salt and pepper and let sit at room temperature for 1 to 2 hours. Stuff the cavity with the bay leaves and celery stalk. Place the chicken, breast-side-up, on a rack in a shallow roasting pan and roast for 15 minutes. Reduce the heat to 375°F and roast until a thermometer inserted into the breast reads 165°F, about 40-45 minutes.

3. Transfer the chicken and rack onto a cutting board, tent with foil to keep warm. Increase oven temperature to 450°F.

4. Pour the drippings from a roasting pan into a heatproof measuring cup or fat separator. Allow the fat to rise to the top. Add a tablespoon of fat to the roasting pan. Heat the roasting pan on top of stove over medium high heat and add the grapes, swirling to soften them slightly. Add the remaining ½ cup of wine to the pan and bring to a boil, scraping the browned bits from the bottom of the pan. Cook until the alcohol has evaporated, about 3 minutes. Add the prepared sauce and simmer, about 2 minutes. Swirl in the remaining tablespoon of cold butter and transfer to a gravy boat to keep warm.

5. Serve the chicken with the grape sauce and toasted pecans.

NUTRITION (PER SERVING):
594 calories, **52 g protein**, 40 g carbohydrates, 3 g fiber, 29 g sugars, 21g fat, 6 g saturated fat, 507 mg sodium

Roasted Chicken with Root Vegetable Stuffing

PREP TIME: 15 minutes **TOTAL TIME:** 2 hours plus resting time Serves 6

1 French baguette

1 whole chicken (3 to 4 pounds)

2 tablespoons extra-virgin olive oil

Kosher salt and ground black pepper to taste

4 tablespoons unsalted butter, divided

1 medium onion, diced

2 medium celery stalks, cut into 1-inch chunks

½ pound mixture of celery root, parsnip, and rutabaga, peeled and diced

½ pound button mushrooms, quartered

1 cup Italian parsley leaves, coarsely chopped

¼ cup loosely packed fresh sage leaves, coarsely chopped

1 to 2 cups low-sodium chicken broth

1. Cut the bread into ½-inch pieces and let dry on two large rimmed baking sheets overnight.

2. Pat the chicken dry inside and out. Make a paste with the oil, 1 teaspoon salt, and ½ teaspoon black pepper. Slide your hand under the chicken's skin to loosen it from the breast and thigh meat. Rub the some of the paste over the breast and thigh meat, careful not to tear the skin. Rub the remaining paste all over the chicken, inside and out, and set on a rack in a roasting pan and refrigerate, uncovered, overnight.

3. In a 5- to 6-quart heavy pot, melt half the butter over medium heat. Cook the onion with a pinch of salt and pepper until transparent, about 5 minutes. Add the celery, root vegetables, and mushrooms and cook, stirring occasionally, until the vegetables have softened, about 15 minutes. Add the herbs and 1 cup stock and bring to a boil. Season to taste with salt and pepper.

4. Transfer the bread to a large bowl. Add the vegetable mixture and mix well with a large wooden spoon. To test for consistency, try to squeeze a bit in your hand to form a ball. If too dry to hold together, adjust with additional stock. Place the stuffing in a casserole and dot with the remaining butter.

5. Heat the oven to 425°F. Roast the chicken for 15 minutes; reduce the heat to 350°F, baste the chicken occasionally with pan drippings until an instant read thermometer inserted into the thigh meat registers 165°F, about 1 hour. Put the stuffing in the oven and roast until warmed through and crispy on top, about 30 minutes. Let the chicken rest 15 minutes before carving.

NUTRITION (PER SERVING):

488 calories, **39 g protein**, 47 g carbs, 4 g fiber, 3 g sugars, 17 g fat, 7 g saturated fat, 836 mg sodium

Chicken in a Pot

PREP TIME: 10 minutes **TOTAL TIME:** 1 hour, 45 minutes Serves 6 to 8

1 whole chicken (3 to 4 pounds)

2 yellow onions, coarsely chopped

2 medium carrots, coarsely chopped

2 celery ribs, coarsely chopped

1 fennel bulb, trimmed and thinly sliced

3 cloves garlic

3 bay leaves

2 sprigs thyme

2 teaspoons kosher salt

¾ teaspoon ground black pepper

1 cup basmati rice

¼ cup fresh parsley and/ or dill, chopped

1. Place the chicken in an 8- to 10-quart pot and cover with water by an inch. Bring to a boil, reduce the heat to a simmer and cook for 30 minutes. Skim the surface of any foam that may form.

2. Add the onions, carrots, celery, fennel, garlic, bay leaves, thyme, salt, and pepper. Bring back to a simmer, and cook until the broth is flavorful, about 1 hour. Meanwhile, cook the rice according to package directions.

3. Transfer the chicken to a cutting board, remove and discard the skin, and either shred the meat or leave it in large chunks. Discard the thyme sprigs, bay leaves, and garlic. Add the chicken back to the pot. Season to taste with salt and pepper.

4. Serve with the cooked rice, and top with parsley or dill.

Note: Lovingly referred to as Jewish Penicillin, this dish has all the fixings to make you feel healthy and whole. A touch of fennel helps make it feel light and springy, but you can add whichever spice you like. (Try it with ginger instead; it's crazy good!) Change out the rice for whatever, noodle, dumpling, pasta or matzo ball.

NUTRITION (PER SERVING):
288 calories, **26 g protein**, 39 g carbs, 4 g fiber, 3 g sugars, 4 g fat, 1 g saturated fat, 791 mg sodium

Chicken in Riesling with Pancetta and Shallots

PREP TIME: 5 minutes **TOTAL TIME:** 1 hour 15 minutes Serves 8

2 ounces diced pancetta

1 whole chicken (3 to 4 pounds), cut into 8 pieces (2 drumsticks, 2 thighs, 2 breasts cut in half, one with the wing portion and the other the lower half)

½ teaspoon kosher salt

½ teaspoon ground black pepper

12 ounces mixed wild mushrooms, trimmed and sliced

2 medium shallots, cut into ½-inch wedges

2 medium carrots, cut into 1-inch chunks on a diagonal

1 small fennel bulb, trimmed and cut into ½-inch wedges, fronds reserved

2 sprigs thyme

1 bay leaf

2 cups dry Riesling

1 cup lower-sodium chicken broth

1 tablespoon unsalted butter

1 tablespoon all-purpose flour

1. In a 5- to 6-quart Dutch oven over medium heat, cook the pancetta until crisp, about 7 minutes. Meanwhile, season the chicken generously with salt and pepper. Using a slotted spoon, transfer the pancetta to a plate.

2. Raise the heat to medium-high and add the chicken pieces, skin side down. Cook until the skin is golden and crisp, about 5 minutes. Flip and cook until golden, another 5 minutes. Transfer the chicken to the plate with the pancetta.

3. Add the mushrooms, shallots, carrots, and fennel to the pan and cook, stirring and scraping up the browned bits on the bottom of the pan, until the mushrooms are browned and their liquid has evaporated, about 10 minutes.

4. Return the chicken pieces and pancetta to the pan and add the thyme and bay leaf. Pour in the Riesling and broth and bring to a boil. Reduce to a simmer, cover, and cook until the chicken is tender, checking the breast after the first 20 minutes. As the pieces are ready, 20 to 35 minutes, transfer to a serving platter and tent with foil to keep warm.

5. Using a slotted spoon, transfer the vegetables to the platter with the chicken. Discard the thyme sprigs and bay leaf. Bring the broth to a boil and reduce by half, about 7 minutes.

6. In a small bowl mash together the butter and flour. Reduce the heat to a simmer and add the butter mixture in small amounts, whisking constantly until the broth is thickened. Season with salt and pepper, pour over and around the chicken, and garnish with fennel fronds.

NUTRITION (PER SERVING):

414 calories, **29 g protein**, 12 g carbohydrates, 2 g fiber, 2 g sugars, 24 g fat, 7.5 g saturated fat, 409 mg sodium

LOVE YOUR LEFTOVER CHICKEN

Thai Peanut Noodles with Chicken and Scallions

PREP TIME: 5 minutes **TOTAL TIME:** 20 minutes Serves 2

4 ounces whole wheat spaghetti

3 tablespoons natural creamy peanut butter

2 tablespoons low-sodium soy sauce

1 tablespoon fresh lime juice

1 to 2 teaspoons Sriracha

1 teaspoon dark brown sugar

1 teaspoon toasted sesame oil

1 cup shredded rotisserie or cooked chicken (light and/or dark meat)

4 thinly sliced scallions

1. Cook the spaghetti according to package directions until al dente; reserve ¼ cup of the cooking water and drain the noodles.

2. Meanwhile, in a large bowl, whisk together the peanut butter, soy sauce, lime juice, Sriracha, brown sugar, sesame oil, and 2 tablespoons of the reserved pasta water until smooth. Add the noodles to the bowl and toss in the sauce until well coated. Toss in the chicken and half the scallions adding more pasta water if needed to loosen the sauce. Divide between 2 bowls and top with the remaining scallions.

NUTRITION (PER SERVING):

517 calories, **37 g protein**, 54 g carbohydrates, 9 g fiber, 7 g sugar, 18 g fat, 2.5 g saturated fat, 778 mg sodium

Zucchini Noodles with Pesto, Chicken, and Chickpeas

PREP TIME: 5 minutes **TOTAL TIME:** 10 minutes Serves 2

2 packed cups fresh basil leaves

¼ cup coarsely grated Parmigiano-Reggiano

2 tablespoons almonds

1 clove garlic

1 teaspoon fresh lemon juice; more to taste

½ teaspoon kosher salt

¼ teaspoon ground black pepper

2 tablespoons water

2 tablespoons extra-virgin olive oil

2 medium zucchini or summer squash, noodled, or 6 cups zucchini noodles

1 can (15 ounces) chickpeas, rinsed and drained

1 cup shredded cooked or rotisserie chicken (light and/or dark meat)

1. Combine the basil, cheese, almonds, garlic, lemon juice, salt, and pepper in a food processor and pulse to finely chop. With the motor running, slowly drizzle in the water and oil until a thick paste forms. Transfer to a large bowl and season to taste with salt, pepper, and more lemon juice, if needed.

2. Add the zucchini noodles, chickpeas, and chicken and gently toss to coat. Serve cold or room temperature.

NUTRITION (PER SERVING):

532 calories, **40 g protein**, 34 g carbohydrates, 9 g fiber, 6 g sugar, 27 g fat, 5 g saturated fat, 831 mg sodium

Arroz con Pollo

PREP TIME: 10 minutes **TOTAL TIME:** 25 minutes Serves 2

1 tablespoon extra-virgin olive oil

1 medium yellow onion, finely chopped

1 medium red bell pepper, finely chopped

2 cloves garlic, minced

½ teaspoon ground cumin

½ teaspoon kosher salt

¼ teaspoon ground black pepper

½ cup canned tomato sauce (not pasta sauce)

½ cup water

2 cups shredded cooked or rotisserie chicken (light and/or dark meat)

1 cup thawed frozen green peas

1 cup cooked brown rice

1. Heat the oil in a large skillet over medium heat. Add the onion, red pepper, and garlic and cook, stirring, until the vegetables are soft, about 5 minutes. Stir in the cumin, salt, and black pepper until fragrant, about 1 minute. Stir in the tomato sauce and water; bring to a simmer. Add the chicken and stir to coat. Cover and cook until the sauce has thickened slightly, about 5 minutes.

2. Stir in the peas and cook until bright green and warmed through, about 2 minutes. Season to taste with salt and pepper. Transfer the rice to a serving platter and top with the chicken mixture.

NUTRITION (PER SERVING):

516 calories, **52 g protein**, 45 g carbs, 8 g fiber, 11 g sugar, 14 g fat, 3 g saturated fat, 750 mg sodium

California Chinese Chicken Salad

PREP TIME: 10 minutes **TOTAL TIME:** 15 minutes Serves 4

½ cup sesame dressing

¼ cup water

2½ cups shredded Napa cabbage

2½ cups shredded lacinato kale

2 cups shredded rotisserie or cooked chicken (light and/or dark meat)

1 cup mung bean sprouts

1 cup grated carrots

2 scallions, sliced

½ cup chow mein noodles

1 avocado, sliced

4 teaspoons sesame seeds

In a large bowl, whisk together the dressing with the water. Add the Napa cabbage, kale, chicken, bean sprouts, carrot, scallions, and chow mein noodles to the bowl, and toss well. Divide between 4 bowls, and top each with ¼ avocado and 1 teaspoon sesame seeds.

NUTRITION (PER SERVING):

390 calories, **26 g protein**, 20 g carbs, 7 g fiber, 8 g sugar, 25 g fat, 3.5 g saturated fat, 643 mg sodium

Chicken Empanadas with Avocado Sauce

PREP TIME: 5 minutes **TOTAL TIME:** 30 minutes Serves 2

For the empanadas:

1 teaspoon olive oil

¼ cup chopped onion

1 clove garlic, minced

½ cup chopped mushrooms

½ cup (2½ ounces) diced cooked or rotisserie chicken (light and/or dark meat)

½ teaspoon fresh thyme leaves

Pinch of salt

Pinch of ground black pepper

4 frozen empanada discs (such as Goya), thawed

4 teaspoons Giblet Gravy (page 95), chilled or store-bought chicken gravy

1 egg, beaten

For the avocado sauce:

1 avocado

Juice of 1 lime

¼ cup cilantro, chopped

1 clove garlic, chopped

1 jalapeno pepper, chopped and seeded (optional)

Pinch of kosher salt

1 to 4 tablespoons water

1. To make the empanadas: Heat the oven to 400°F. Line a baking sheet with parchment paper.

2. In a medium skillet, heat the oil until shimmering. Cook the onion and garlic until translucent, about 3 minutes. Add the mushrooms and cook until they release liquid, about 2 minutes. Add the chicken, thyme, salt, and pepper, stirring to combine. Set aside to cool slightly.

3. Place the empanada discs on a flat surface. Spoon 1 teaspoon of gravy in the center of each disc, then divide the chicken mixture among them. Fold each disc in half and seal the edges with a fork. Brush with the egg and place on the prepared baking sheet. Bake until golden, 15 to 20 minutes.

4. To make the avocado sauce: Combine the avocado, lime juice, cilantro, garlic, jalapeno (if using), and a pinch of salt in a blender. Add water, 1 tablespoon at a time, until the sauce thins to desired consistency.

5. Serve the empanadas warm, with the avocado sauce.

NUTRITION (PER SERVING):

528 calories, **23 g protein**, 58 g carbohydrates, 5 g fiber, 4 g sugar, 25 g fat, 6.5 g sat, 431 mg sodium

Chicken and Green Veggie Pot Pie

PREP TIME: 20 minutes **TOTAL TIME:** 1 hour 15 minutes Serves 6

For the crust:

1¼ cup whole wheat flour

¼ cup finely grated Parmesan

1 tablespoon chopped fresh thyme

½ teaspoon kosher salt

½ teaspoon ground black pepper

6 tablespoons cold unsalted butter, diced

4 to 6 tablespoons ice water

For the filling:

¼ cup olive oil

½ yellow onion, chopped

¼ cup all-purpose flour

1 tablespoon chopped fresh thyme

1 tablespoon chopped fresh sage

½ teaspoon kosher salt

½ teaspoon ground black pepper

2½ cups low-sodium chicken broth, heated

2 cups shredded cooked or rotisserie chicken (light and/or dark meat)

2 cups torn kale leaves

2 cups broccoli florets

1 cup frozen green beans

1. To make the crust: In a medium bowl, stir together the flour, cheese, thyme, salt, and pepper. With a pastry blender or two knives, cut the butter into the dry mixture until it resembles a coarse meal. Add the ice water 1 tablespoon at a time until the dough comes together. (Alternatively, in a food processor, pulse the butter into the dry ingredients, then pulse in the water 1 tablespoon at a time.) Transfer the dough to a large piece of plastic wrap, form into a disk, and wrap tightly. Chill for 30 minutes.

2. To make the filling: Heat the oven to 375°F. In a medium pot, heat the oil over medium heat. Add the onion and cook until translucent and soft, about 7 minutes. Add the flour and cook until it bubbles and smells nutty, about 30 seconds. Stir in the thyme, sage, salt, and pepper and cook until fragrant, another 30 seconds. Whisk in the broth and cook until thickened, about 5 minutes. Remove from the heat and stir in the chicken, kale, broccoli, and green beans. Transfer the mixture to a 10" deep-dish pie plate or 8" x 8"-inch baking dish .

3. On a lightly floured surface, roll the crust into 12" round and gently place on top of the pie filling. Press the edges of the dough down against the top of the pie plate to seal. Trim the dough, flute the edges, and slice vents in the top. Place the pie onto a baking sheet and bake until the crust is golden and the filling is bubbling, about 40 minutes. Cool 15 minutes before serving.

NUTRITION (PER SERVING):

425 calories, **24 g protein**, 29 g carbohydrates, 5 g fiber, 1 g sugars, 25 g fat, 10 g saturated fat, 455 mg sodium

Chicken and Fig Grilled Cheese

PREP TIME: 5 minutes **TOTAL TIME:** 10 minutes Serves 2

1 tablespoon unsalted butter

4 slices whole-grain bread

2 tablespoons fig preserves

1 teaspoon dried thyme or minced fresh rosemary

½ cup shredded cooked or rotisserie chicken (light and/or dark meat)

1 cup baby spinach

2 ounces brie cheese, rind removed, or ⅔ cup shredded Fontina

Melt the butter in a skillet over medium heat. Spread 1 tablespoon fig preserves on each of 2 slices whole-grain bread. Sprinkle each with the thyme or rosemary. Top with half the chicken, half the spinach, half the cheese, and a second bread slice. Place in the skillet and heat until bread is golden and crispy on both sides and cheese has melted, 2 to 3 minutes per side.

NUTRITION (PER SERVING, WITH BRIE):
405 calories, **25 g protein**, 37 g carbohydrates, 5 g fiber, 13 g sugar, 17 g fat, 9.5 g saturated fat, 494 mg sodium

NUTRITION (PER SERVING, WITH FONTINA):
450 calories, **28 g protein**, 38 g carbohydrates, 5 g fiber, 13 g sugar, 21 g fat, 11.5 g saturated fat, 603 mg sodium

Apple Chicken Grilled Cheese

PREP TIME: 5 minutes **TOTAL TIME:** 10 minutes Serves 2

1 tablespoon unsalted butter

4 slices country bread

2 ounces thinly sliced asiago or fontina cheese

1 cup sliced rotisserie or cooked chicken (light and/or dark meat)

1 small apple, thinly sliced

⅔ cup arugula

Melt the butter in a skillet over medium heat. Top 2 slices of the bread each with half the cheese, ½ cup chicken, ½ apple, and half the arugula. Top with the other 2 slices of bread. Place in the skillet and heat until the cheese is melted and the bread is golden brown, 2 to 3 minutes per side.

NUTRITION (PER SERVING, WITH ASIAGO):
517 calories, **36 g protein**, 51 g carbohydrates, 6 g fiber, 14 g sugars, 19 g fat, 9.5 g saturated fat, 989 mg sodium

NUTRITION (PER SERVING, WITH FONTINA):
526 calories, **36 g protein**, 51 g carbohydrates, 6 g fiber, 14 g sugars, 19 g fat, 9.5 g saturated fat, 972 mg sodium

Caprese Chicken Pasta

PREP TIME: 5 minutes **TOTAL TIME:** 20 minutes Serves 2

4 ounces whole-grain penne (or 2 cups cooked)

1 cup shredded rotisserie or cooked chicken (light and/or dark meat)

1 pint cherry tomatoes, halved

2 ounces fresh mozzarella pearls

2 tablespoons olive oil

2 tablespoons balsamic vinegar

⅓ cup thinly sliced fresh basil

¼ teaspoon ground black pepper

1. Cook the pasta according to package directions. Drain and transfer to a medium bowl.

2. Toss together the penne, chicken, tomatoes, and mozzarella.

3. In a separate bowl, whisk together the olive oil, vinegar, basil, and pepper. Toss the dressing with the pasta.

NUTRITION (PER SERVING):

548 calories, **34 g protein**, 50 g carbohydrates, 8 g fiber, 6 g sugars, 24 g fat, 6.5 g saturated fat, 339 mg sodium

Caprese Chicken Pasta

Chicken and Mushroom Ragu over Polenta

PREP TIME: 10 minutes **TOTAL TIME:** 25 minutes Serves 2

2 tablespoons olive oil

8 ounces sliced mushrooms

1 small shallot, diced

½ teaspoon chopped fresh rosemary

2 tablespoons tomato paste

⅔ cup dry red wine

1 cup shredded rotisserie or cooked chicken (light and/or dark meat)

1 cup baby kale

½ teaspoon kosher salt + more to taste

¼ teaspoon ground black pepper + more to taste

½ cup instant polenta

1½ cups low-sodium chicken broth

1 tablespoon grated pecorino Romano, for serving

1. Heat the olive oil in a large skillet over medium. Add the mushrooms, shallot, and rosemary and cook until golden, about 8 minutes. Stir in the tomato paste and cook until the paste darkens a shade, about 1 minute. Add the wine, bring to a boil, and cook until thick, saucy, and shiny, 2 to 3 minutes. Add the chicken, kale, salt, and pepper, and cook until the kale is wilted and the chicken is heated through, 2 to 3 minutes more. Keep warm.

2. Meanwhile, prepare the polenta with the broth according to package directions; season to taste with salt and pepper.

3. Place the cooked polenta in serving bowls and top with the chicken mixture and grated cheese.

NUTRITION (PER SERVING):
577 calories, **32 g protein**, 62 g carbohydrates, 5 g fiber, 6 g sugars, 18 g fat, 3.5 g saturated fat, 969 mg sodium

Chicken Quinoa Soup

PREP TIME: 10 minutes **TOTAL TIME:** 40 minutes Serves 6

2 leeks, light greens thinly sliced, dark tops discarded

3 carrots, chopped

2 ribs celery, sliced

1 tablespoon unsalted butter

1 cup white wine

6 cups low-sodium chicken broth

¾ cup quinoa

1½ teaspoons Cajun seasoning

1" to 2" piece of Parmesan rind (optional)

2 cups chopped rotisserie or cooked chicken (light and/or dark meat)

3 cups baby spinach

Juice of ½ lemon + more to taste

½ teaspoon kosher salt + more to taste

¼ teaspoon ground black pepper + to taste

¼ cup parsley, chopped, for garnish

In a large saucepan over medium heat, cook the leeks, carrots, celery, in the butter until tender, about 5 minutes. Add the wine; simmer until reduced by half, 3 to 5 minutes. Add the broth, quinoa, Cajun seasoning, and Parmesan rind (if using); simmer, covered, until the quinoa is tender, 15 to 20 minutes. Stir in the chicken, spinach, lemon juice, salt, and pepper; heat for 2 minutes. Remove the rind, if using; taste to adjust lemon juice and seasoning. Serve garnished with the parsley.

NUTRITION (PER SERVING):

386 calories, **34 g protein**, 40 g carbohydrates, 6 g fiber, 7 g fat, 1.5 g saturated fat, 882 mg sodium

Asian Chicken Noodle Soup

PREP TIME: 10 minutes **TOTAL TIME:** 20 minutes Serves 6

3 tablespoons canola oil

2 tablespoons grated fresh ginger

2 cloves garlic, minced

1 small rotisserie chicken (no skin), meat shredded

1 quart low-sodium chicken broth

2 cups water

2 tablespoons lime juice

1 to 2 tablespoons fish sauce

5 ounces greens (such as baby spinach), chopped

1 package (about 8 ounces) glass noodles

¼ cup cilantro or 2 scallions, chopped

1. In a large soup pot over medium, heat the oil, ginger, and garlic until fragrant, 2 to 3 minutes. Add the shredded chicken, chicken broth, and water and simmer until warmed through, 5 to 7 minutes. Stir in the lime juice and fish sauce. Add the greens and cook until just wilted, 2 minutes.

2. Meanwhile, prepare the noodles according to package and drain.

3. Divide the prepared noodles among 6 soup bowls. Ladle the soup into the bowls and top with cilantro or scallions.

NUTRITION (PER SERVING):

447 calories, **43 g protein**, 37 g carbohydrates, 1 g fiber, 0 g sugars, 14 g fat, 2.5 g saturated fat, 817 mg sodium

Asian-Style Chili Chicken "Nachos"

PREP TIME: 10 minutes **TOTAL TIME:** 10 minutes Serves 2

¼ cup hoisin sauce

2 tablespoons fresh lime juice

1 teaspoon Sriracha

1 cup leftover grilled or roasted chicken breast, shredded

24 sesame rice crackers

½ cup shredded napa cabbage

½ cup grated daikon radish

1 mini cucumber, thinly sliced

1 small red chile, thinly sliced

1 scallion, sliced

¼ cup cilantro leaves

2 tablespoons sour cream (optional)

2 lime wedges, for garnish

1. In a medium microwave-safe bowl, stir together the hoisin sauce, lime juice, and Sriracha. Add the chicken and stir to coat it in the sauce. Cover and microwave for 1 minute.

2. Pile the rice crackers in the middle of a large plate and top with the chicken, cabbage, radish, cucumber, chile, scallion, and cilantro. Serve with the sour cream, if using, and lime wedges.

NUTRITION (PER SERVING):

330 calories, **26 g protein**, 40 g carbs, 2 g fiber, 13 g sugars, 7 g fat, 2 g saturated fat, 693 mg sodium

Green Envy Rice Bowl

PREP TIME: 10 minutes **TOTAL TIME:** 40 minutes Serves 4

1 pound asparagus, trimmed and chopped

1 onion, chopped

½ pound brussels sprouts, trimmed and halved

½ pound cremini or button mushrooms, halved (quartered if large)

2 tablespoons olive oil

1 teaspoon ground cumin

1 teaspoon smoked paprika

1 teaspoon garlic powder

1 teaspoon kosher salt

2 cups cooked brown rice

2 cups diced or shredded leftover cooked or rotisserie chicken (light and/or dark meat)

1 cup kimchi, optional

1 avocado, sliced

4 tablespoons Tahini Garlic Dressing (below)

1. Heat the oven to 425°F.

2. On a baking sheet, combine the asparagus, onion, Brussels sprouts, and mushrooms with the olive oil, cumin, smoked paprika, garlic powder, and salt. Spread out on the baking sheet, tossing once, and roast until the veggies are slightly charred, 25 to 30 minutes.

3. Divide the rice among 4 bowls. Top each with ½ cup chicken, ¼ cup kimchi (if using), and ¼ avocado. Drizzle with 1 tablespoon dressing.

NUTRITION (PER SERVING):

478 calories, **31 g protein**, 40 g carbohydrates, 9 g fiber, 5 g sugar, 23 g fat, 3.5 g saturated fat, 623 mg sodium

Tahini Garlic Dressing

PREP TIME: 5 minutes **TOTAL TIME:** 5 minutes Serves 12

¼ cup tahini

¼ cup olive oil

¼ cup apple cider vinegar

2 or 3 cloves garlic, minced

1 teaspoon miso paste

¼ teaspoon salt

¼ teaspoon ground black pepper.

Water, as necessary

In a glass jar, combine the tahini, olive oil, and apple cider vinegar. Add the garlic, miso, salt, and pepper. Thin with water to desired consistency. Store in the fridge for up to 1 week. Makes ¾ cup.

Note: This flavorful dressing can be drizzled on savory bowls and salads. If you don't have miso, sub in ½ teaspoon sea salt.

NUTRITION (PER SERVING):

74 calories, **1 g protein**, 2 g carbohydrates, 0 g fiber, 0 g sugar, 7 g fat, 1 g sat, 68 mg sodium

Green Envy Rice Bowl

Chicken, Barley, and Broccolini Soup

PREP TIME: 10 minutes **TOTAL TIME:** 30 minutes Serves 2

¼ cup quick-cooking barley

1 tablespoon olive oil

1 medium leek, dark green parts removed, white stalk halved lengthwise, thinly sliced, and rinsed

2 ribs celery, thinly sliced

1 clove garlic, minced

1 bunch (6 ounces) broccolini, trimmed and cut into 2-inch pieces

1 small sprig rosemary

1 bay leaf

½ teaspoon kosher salt + more to taste

½ teaspoon ground black pepper + more for serving

1 quart low-sodium chicken broth

2 cups baby kale

1 cup chunks leftover or rotisserie chicken (light and/or dark meat)

¼ cup coarsely chopped fresh flat-leaf parsley

2 tablespoons tiny basil leaves or thinly sliced basil

1. Cook the barley according to package directions. Drain and rinse under cool water.

2. Meanwhile, in a medium saucepan over medium heat, heat the oil until shimmering. Add the leek, celery, and garlic and cook, stirring, until the vegetables soften, about 5 minutes.

3. Stir the broccolini, rosemary, bay leaf, salt, and pepper to coat with the leek mixture, about 2 minutes. Add the broth, bring to a boil, and reduce to a simmer. Cook until the broccolini is tender but still bright green, about 5 minutes.

4. Add the kale, chicken, and cooked barley to warm through, about 5 minutes. Remove and discard the bay leaf and rosemary sprig. Stir in the parsley and season to taste with salt. Ladle into bowls and top with the basil and more black pepper to taste.

NUTRITION (PER SERVING):

360 calories, **33 g protein**, 34 g carbohydrates, 6 g fiber, 5 g sugar, 10 g fat, 2 g saturated fat, 810 mg sodium

Vietnamese-Style Pulled Chicken Sandwiches

PREP TIME: 15 minutes **TOTAL TIME:** 25 minutes Serves 4

2 tablespoons toasted sesame oil

1 tablespoon fish sauce

½ teaspoon less-sodium soy sauce

4 soft hoagie, Portuguese,or Cuban rolls (5 inches long), split

¼ red onion, cut into ¼-inch-thick rings

¼ cup fresh cilantro leaves

1½ cups shredded leftover or rotisserie chicken breast (without skin)

1 cup kimchi, drained

4 butter lettuce or bibb lettuce leaves

2 tablespoons mayonnaise

1. Heat a large skillet over medium. In a small bowl, mix together the sesame oil, fish sauce, and soy sauce and brush on the cut sides of the rolls. Place the rolls, cut side down, in the skillet (if all 4 rolls do not fit, do this in batches). Toast for 3 minutes, or until golden and crispy.

2. Arrange the red onion, cilantro, chicken, kimchi, and lettuce on the bottom half of the rolls. Spread the top half of the rolls with the mayonnaise. Close up the sandwiches and serve.

Note: If you prefer less spice, use mild kimchi (fermented cabbage). It's packed with flavor and good-for-you probiotic bacteria. Look for it in the produce section of most grocery stores. These sandwiches are best with a softer roll typical of those you'd find in the packaged bread and roll aisle in most grocery stores—not in the fresh bakery section.

NUTRITION (PER SERVING):

415 calories, **24 g protein**, 36 g carbohydrates, 3 g fiber, 4 g sugar, 19 g fat, 4 g saturated fat, 1121 mg sodium

Spring Chicken Rainbow Slaw
with Buttermilk Dressing

Spring Chicken Rainbow Slaw with Buttermilk Dressing

PREP TIME: 10 minutes **TOTAL TIME:** 15 minutes Serves 2

½ cup low-fat buttermilk

4 teaspoons fresh lemon juice or white wine vinegar

1 clove garlic minced with ¼ teaspoon kosher salt

1 teaspoon honey mustard

¼ teaspoon ground black pepper

1 cup shredded roasted or rotisserie chicken (light and/or dark meat)

1 cup thinly sliced red cabbage

2 small carrots, grated

2 small rainbow or Chioggia beets, scrubbed and very thinly sliced

1 avocado, vertically sliced

½ cup snow pea shoots

1. In a medium bowl, whisk together the buttermilk, lemon juice, salty garlic, mustard, and pepper.

2. Add the chicken and toss to coat. Arrange on 2 large plates with the cabbage, carrots, beets, avocado, and pea shoots and season with salt and pepper. Drizzle with remaining dressing in the bowl and toss before eating.

NUTRITION (PER SERVING):
322 calories, **25 g protein**, 27 g carbs, 9 g fiber, 13 g sugar, 14 g fat, 3 g saturated fat, 479 mg sodium

Tex-Mex Pizzas

PREP TIME: 10 minutes **TOTAL TIME:** 15 minutes Serves 2

6 tablespoons canned refried beans

2 corn tostadas

5 tablespoons prepared salsa

1 ounces shredded Monterey jack cheese

½ cup (packed) shredded rotisserie or cooked chicken (light and/or dark meat)

¼ cup thawed frozen corn

¼ cup sour cream

2 tablespoons fresh lime juice

½ avocado, sliced

1 scallion, sliced

1. Heat the broiler to high.

2. Spread the beans on the tostadas and set on a baking sheet. Top each with half the salsa, cheese, chicken, and corn. Broil until cheese has melted, about 2 minutes.

3. In a small bowl, combine the sour cream with the lime juice.

4. Serve the tostadas topped with the avocado, scallion, and a drizzle of the sour cream mixture.

NUTRITION (PER SERVING):
344 calories, **21 g protein**, 26 g carbohydrates, 6 g fiber, 4 g sugar, 19 g fat, 7.5 g saturated fat, 797 mg sodium

Chicken Pesto Pizza

PREP TIME: 10 minutes **TOTAL TIME:** 20 minutes Serves 4

1 tablespoon cornmeal

1 pound refrigerated whole wheat pizza dough

⅓ cup prepared pesto

1½ cups small strips of cooked or rotisseries chicken breast (without skin)

1 roasted red pepper, cut into small strips

½ cup marinated and quartered artichoke hearts, drained

2 ounces crumbled goat cheese

1. Heat the oven to 450°F. Coat a large pizza pan or baking sheet with cooking spray. Sprinkle with the cornmeal. Turn the dough out onto a lightly floured work surface and roll into a 12" circle. Place on the prepared baking sheet.

2. Spread the dough with the pesto, leaving a ¼-inch border. Top with the chicken, pepper strips, and artichokes. Dot with the goat cheese. Bake until the cheese is melted and the crust is golden brown, about 10 minutes.

NUTRITION (PER SERVING):

503 calories, **32 g protein**, 54 g carbohydrates, 9 g fiber, 1 g sugar, 20 g fat, 6 g saturated fat, 871 mg sodium

Thai Chicken Pizza

PREP TIME: 15 minutes **TOTAL TIME:** 25 minutes Serves 4

8 ounces refrigerated pizza dough

¾ cup Thai red curry sauce

1¼ cups shredded roasted or rotisserie chicken (light and/or dark meat)

½ cup shredded carrots

½ cup thinly sliced red bell pepper

½ small red onion, thinly sliced

¼ cup (2 ounces) shredded Monterey jack cheese

Fresh scallions (optional)

1. Heat the oven to 500°F. Coat a baking sheet with cooking spray and set aside.

2. On a lightly floured surface, roll out the pizza dough into a very thin 15" x 11" rectangle or oval. Place on the baking sheet. Spread the curry sauce almost to the edges of the dough. Sprinkle with the chicken, carrots, bell pepper, onion, and cheese. Bake until the dough is golden and crisp, about 8 minutes. Top with fresh scallions when serving, if desired.

NUTRITION (PER SERVING):
287 calories, **20 g protein**, 33 g carbohydrates, 2 g fiber, 7 g sugar, 8 g fat, 4.5 g saturated fat, 828 mg sodium

Thai Chicken Pizza

Waldorf Chicken Salad Wraps

PREP TIME: 10 minutes **TOTAL TIME:** 10 minutes Serves 2

1¼ cup chopped roasted or rotisserie chicken breast

½ apple, chopped

1 rib celery, chopped

⅓ cup seedless green grapes, halved

¼ cup mayonnaise

2 tablespoons chopped toasted walnuts

1 teaspoon lemon juice

Kosher salt and ground black pepper

2 (8-inch) whole wheat or whole-grain tortillas

2 leaves Bibb or Boston lettuce, coarsely shredded

In a medium bowl, combine the chicken, apple, celery, grapes, mayonnaise, walnuts, and lemon juice. Stir until all ingredients are coated. Season to taste with salt and pepper. To serve, scoop half the chicken salad onto the bottom third of each tortilla and top with half the lettuce. Roll up from the bottom, tucking in the sides as you go.

NUTRITION (PER SERVING):

553 calories, **32 g protein**, 35 g carbohydrates, 5 g fiber, 9 g sugar, 32 g fat, 5.5 g saturated fat, 649 mg sodium

Waldorf Chicken
Salad Wraps

GROUND CHICKEN & SAUSAGE GOODNESS

Chicken Sausage and Apple Power Salad

PREP TIME: 5 minutes **TOTAL TIME:** 10 minutes Serves 2

1 teaspoon + 2 tablespoons olive oil

2 chicken apple sausages (such as Applegate), diagonally sliced

Juice of ½ lemon

1 teaspoon minced fresh sage

⅛ teaspoon kosher salt + more to taste

⅛ teaspoon ground black pepper + to taste

¼ head romaine (5 to 6 ounces), chopped

1 cup (about 1½ ounces) watercress

½ apple, sliced

½ cup cooked quinoa

1. In a medium skillet, heat 1 teaspoon of the oil over medium. Add the sausages and cook until browned on both sides, about 5 minutes.

2. Meanwhile, in a large bowl whisk together the remaining olive oil with the lemon juice, sage, salt, and pepper. Add the romaine and watercress and toss. Divide between plates, and top each with the apple, quinoa, and sausage.

NUTRITION (PER SERVING):

397 calories, **20 g protein**, 27 g carbohydrates, 5 g fiber, 6 g sugar, 24 g fat, 4.5 g saturated fat, 639 mg sodium

Chicken Salad Casserole

PREP TIME: 10 minutes **TOTAL TIME:** 1 hour Serves 6

1 tablespoon olive oil

1 onion, chopped

1 green bell pepper, chopped

1 red bell pepper, chopped

1 yellow bell pepper, chopped

1 can or box (10.5 ounces to 12 ounces) condensed cream of mushroom soup

½ cup mayonnaise

½ cup sour cream

2 tablespoons lemon juice

2 cups chopped cooked or rotisserie chicken breast (without skin)

2 cups cooked brown rice

2 hard-cooked eggs, chopped

¼ cup slivered almonds

½ teaspoon kosher salt

¼ teaspoon ground black pepper

1½ cups baked potato chips, crushed

1. Heat the oven to 350°F. Coat a 2- to 3-quart baking dish with cooking spray.

2. Heat the oil in a large skillet over medium-high. Cook the onion and bell peppers until tender, about 6 minutes.

3. In a large bowl, whisk together the soup, mayonnaise, sour cream, and lemon juice. Stir in the onion-pepper mixture, chicken, rice, eggs, almonds, salt, and pepper just until blended. Pour into the baking dish and sprinkle with the potato chips.

4. Bake until hot and bubbling, 30 to 35 minutes. Let stand for 10 minutes before serving.

NUTRITION (PER SERVING):

499 calories, **22 g protein**, 32 g carbohydrates, 4 g fiber, 5 g sugar, 31 g fat, 6.5 g saturated fat, 728 mg sodium

Chicken Gauc Breakfast Nachos

PREP TIME: 5 minutes **TOTAL TIME:** 10 minutes Serves 2

3 ounces tortilla chips

2 pinches chipotle chili powder

1 ounce grated Cheddar

1 tablespoon + 1 teaspoon canola oil

¼ pound ground chicken

3 tablespoons chopped red onion

⅛ teaspoon kosher salt

⅛ teaspoon pepper

2 large eggs

¼ cup guacamole

1 tablespoon hot sauce

2 tablespoons chopped roasted red peppers

3 tablespoons cilantro

1. Toss the tortilla chips onto a tray and into a 350° oven or toaster oven to warm through, about 2 to 3 minutes. Toss with a pinch of chili powder, top with the cheese and and return to the toaster oven to melt.

2. To a large nonstick skillet over medium-high, add 1 tablespoon of the oil. Add the chicken, onion, salt, pepper, and a pinch of chili powder. Cook until browned, 3 to 4 minutes. Pile a top the chips.

3. Add the remaining oil and the eggs to the skillet and scramble, seasoning with salt and pepper. Spread the eggs over the nachos and top with the guacamole, hot sauce,red peppers, and cilantro.

NUTRITION (PER SERVING):

570 calories, **24 g protein**, 34 g carbs, 4 g fiber, 3 g sugar, 37 g fat, 8 g saturated fat, 742 mg sodium

Orzo Diavolo with Sausage and 'Chokes

PREP TIME: 5 minutes **TOTAL TIME:** 15 minutes Serves 2

4 ounces orzo

8 ounces hot Italian chicken sausage (loose or casings removed)

2 ounces (2 cups) arugula

4 chopped artichoke hearts (in water, drained)

6 peppadews

2 cloves garlic, coarsely chopped

2 tablespoons sherry vinegar

2 tablespoons tomato paste

2 tablespoons olive oil

Crush red pepper flakes, to taste

Shaved pecorino Romano, for serving

1. Cook the orzo according to package directions.

2. Set a second skillet over medium with the sausage, breaking it up and cooking until brown, about 6 minutes. Remove from the heat.

3. Drain the pasta, reserving ⅓ cup water, and add the pasta to the sausage along with the arugula and artichoke hearts.

4. In a blender, combine the reserved pasta water with the peppadews, garlic, vinegar, tomato paste, and olive oil. Toss with the pasta. Sprinkle on red pepper flakes, to taste, and shave the cheese over top.

Note: Look for jarred peppadews, small, slightly sweet, slightly hot red peppers, in the same aisle as you would find pickles and olives. Or check your supermarket's salad bar.

NUTRITION (PER SERVING):

589 calories, **30 g protein**, 63 g carbohydrates, 4 g fiber, 11 g sugar, 26 g fat, 6 g saturated fat, 1046 mg sodium

Dumpling Stir Fry

PREP TIME: 10 minutes **TOTAL TIME:** 15 minutes Serves 2

2 tablespoons olive oil

2 teaspoons minced fresh ginger

¾ pound ground chicken

1 cup snap peas, string removed

1 cup fresh corn kernels

4 to 6 baby bok choy, sliced

1 or 2 fresno chiles, sliced

¼ cup hoisin sauce

1 tablespoon water

Heat the olive oil in a wok or a large skillet over medium-high heat. Add the ginger, and cook for 30 seconds. Add the chicken and cook until no longer pink, about 3 minutes. Add the snap peas, corn, bok choy and chile, and cook until the vegetables are crisp and the chicken is cooked through, about 2 minutes more. Thin the hoisin sauce with the water, then stir into the chicken and vegetables.

NUTRITION (PER SERVING):

547 calories, **37 g protein**, 37 g carbohydrates, 7 g fiber, 17 g sugar, 30 g fat, 6 g saturated fat, 741 mg sodium

Dumpling Stir Fry

Pumpkin and Chicken Chili

PREP TIME: 20 minutes **TOTAL TIME:** 1 hour 10 minutes Serves 12

2 tablespoons olive oil

1 large white onion, diced

½ to 1 jalapeno pepper, minced

3 cloves garlic, minced

2 red bell peppers, diced

2 pounds ground chicken

3 tablespoons chili powder

4 teaspoons ground cumin

2 pounds pumpkin, peeled and diced

2 cans (15.5 ounces each) white kidney beans, drained and rinsed

1 can (28 ounces) fire-roasted diced tomatoes with green chilies

4 or 5 cinnamon sticks

3 or 4 bay leaves

1 teaspoon kosher salt

1 teaspoon ground black pepper

1 cup fat-free plain Greek yogurt, for serving

¼ cup cilantro leaves, for serving

Lime wedges, for serving

1. In a large pot, heat the oil over medium-high. Add the onion, jalapeno, garlic, and bell peppers; cook until tender, about 8 minutes.

2. Add the chicken and cook, breaking up with wooden spoon, until browned, about 5 minutes. Stir in the chili powder and cumin. Cook until fragrant, about 1 minute. Add the pumpkin, beans, tomatoes, cinnamon sticks, bay leaves, salt, and pepper.

3. Cook, partially covered, and stirring occasionally, until the pumpkin is tender and the chili thickens slightly, about 35 minutes. Remove and discard the cinnamon sticks and bay leaves. Serve topped with a dollop of yogurt, fresh cilantro, and lime wedges.

Note: This big-batch recipe can serve a crowd—but it also freezes great. Just cool completely before freezing portions in freezer-safe containers, and thaw overnight in the fridge before using.

NUTRITION (PER SERVING):

236 calories, **20 g protein**, 21 g carbohydrates, 4 g fiber, 6 g sugar, 9 g fat, 2 g saturated fat, 369 mg sodium

Loaded Taco Bowls

PREP TIME: 10 minutes **TOTAL TIME:** 35 minutes Serves 4

⅔ cup quinoa

2 tablespoons olive oil

4 large scallions, sliced, white and green parts kept separate

1 red bell pepper, diced

2 cloves garlic, minced

1 pound ground chicken

1 cup frozen corn kernels

2 tablespoons chili powder

2 teaspoons ground cumin

1 teaspoon kosher salt

1 teaspoon black pepper

1 cup cherry tomatoes, halved

1 jalapeño, sliced

½ cup cilantro leaves

½ cup low fat plain Greek yogurt

¼ cup pepitas

Lime wedges, for serving

1. Cook the quinoa according to package instructions.

2. In a large skillet, heat the oil over medium-high heat. Add the white parts of the scallions, bell pepper, and garlic and cook until the vegetables are softened, about 4 to 5 minutes. Add the chicken and cook, breaking up the meat with a wooden spoon, until the chicken is browned and cooked through, about 4 to 5 minutes. Add the corn, chili powder, cumin, salt, and pepper, stirring well. Remove from the heat.

3. Divide the quinoa among 4 bowls and top with the turkey and vegetable mixture, scallion greens, tomatoes, jalapeno, cilantro, yogurt, and pepitas; serve with lime wedges.

NUTRITION (PER SERVING):
474 calories, **31 g protein**, 40 g carbs, 6 g fiber, 6 g sugar, 23 g fat, 5 g saturated fat, 592 mg sodium

Greek Chicken Tacos

Greek Chicken Tacos

PREP TIME: 5 minutes **TOTAL TIME:** 15 minutes Serves 4

1 tablespoon olive oil
1 pound ground chicken
1 teaspoon dried oregano
½ teaspoon ground black pepper
4 whole-wheat pita breads
1 tomato, diced
½ cucumber, diced
½ cup 2% plain Greek yogurt
1 tablespoon fresh chopped dill
1 teaspoon fresh lemon zest
¼ cup crumbled feta cheese

1. Heat the olive oil in large skillet over medium heat. Add the chicken, oregano, and black pepper and cook until no longer pink, 5 to 6 minutes.

2. Meanwhile, warm the pita breads in a toaster oven, oven, or microwave.

3. Divide the chicken mixture among the pita breads (down the middle, so you can fold up the sides and eat them like tacos). Top each with tomato and cucumber.

4. In a small bowl, combine the yogurt, dill and lemon zest. Drizzle over the tacos and sprinkle with the feta.

NUTRITION (PER SERVING):
422 calories, **31 g protein**, 39 g carbohydrates, 6 g fiber, 3 g sugars, 17 g fat, 5 g saturated fat, 469 mg sodium

Thai Chicken and Cabbage Stir Fry

PREP TIME: 10 minutes **TOTAL TIME:** 25 minutes Serves 4

1½ pounds ground chicken

2 tablespoons green Thai curry paste

1 tablespoon cornstarch

1 teaspoon grated fresh ginger

2 teaspoons lime juice

1 teaspoon lime zest

2 teaspoons vegetable oil, divided

2 cup shredded mixed green and purple cabbage

1 cup shredded or julienned carrots

1 cup bean sprouts

1 Thai chile, sliced

3 scallions, sliced

12 Boston lettuce leaves

Lime wedges, for serving

1. In a large bowl, stir together the chicken, curry paste, cornstarch, ginger, and lime juice and zest.

2. Heat 1 teaspoon of the oil in a large wok over high. Add the chicken mixture and cook, breaking up with a wooden spoon, until the chicken is browned and cooked through, about 5 minutes. Transfer to a plate.

3. Wipe the wok clean, and heat the remaining oil. Add the cabbage, carrots, bean sprouts, and chile and cook, stirring, until crisp tender, about 2 minutes. Add the chicken and cook until reheated. Remove from the heat and stir in the scallions. Serve with lettuce leaves and lime wedges.

Note: Save yourself some hassle and buy already-julienned carrots in the produce section of the supermarket. Thai bird chiles are small red or green chiles that pack a punch! For less heat (and an easier find) try a jalapeno or fresno chile.

NUTRITION (PER SERVING):
317 calories, **32 g protein**, 12 g carbs, 3 g fiber, 5 g sugar, 16 g fat, 4 g saturated fat, 270 mg sodium

Sloppy Joes

PREP TIME: 10 minutes **TOTAL TIME:** 30 minutes Serves 4

For the sloppy joes:

1 tablespoon olive oil

1 medium yellow onion, chopped

3 medium carrots, grated (2 cups)

4 cloves garlic, minced

1 pound ground chicken

1 cup low-sodium chicken broth

½ cup (4 ounces) tomato paste

4 teaspoons chili powder

1 tablespoon Worcestershire sauce

2 teaspoons Dijon mustard

4 whole wheat buns or 8 whole wheat sliders

For a side salad:

8 cups mixed greens

½ cup cherry tomatoes, halved

½ cup store-bought balsamic vinaigrette

1. Heat the oil in a large skillet over medium-high. Add the onion, carrots, and garlic. Cook until tender, 6 minutes.

2. Add the chicken and cook, breaking up with a wooden spoon, until browned, about 5 minutes.

3. Stir in the broth, tomato paste, chili powder, Worcestershire, and mustard and cook until thickened, about 8 minutes.

4. Meanwhile, in a large bowl, toss the greens and tomatoes with the vinaigrette. Serve the sloppy joes on the buns alongside the salad.

NUTRITION (PER SERVING):

518 calories, **28 g protein**, 48 g carbohydrates, 9 g fiber, 14 g sugars, 26 g fat, 5 g saturated fat, 978 mg sodium

Orange Lentils with Chicken Sausage and Greens

PREP TIME: 5 minutes **TOTAL TIME:** 30 minutes Serves 4

1 cup orange or red lentils (masoor dal), or 2 cups cooked lentils

1 tablespoon olive oil

4 chicken-apple sausages

1 yellow onion, thinly sliced

4 cloves garlic, sliced

¾ cup low-sodium chicken broth

½ teaspoon dried thyme

¼ teaspoon ground sage

⅛ teaspoon kosher salt

⅛ teaspoon ground black pepper

1 pound baby spinach

1. Cook the lentils according to package directions.

2. Meanwhile, heat the oil in a large skillet over medium. Add the sausages and onion, and cook until the sausages are browned and the onions are caramelized, about 8 to 10 minutes.

3. Remove the sausages and slice into 1-inch segments. Return to the skillet with the garlic. Cook until fragrant, about 30 to 60 seconds.

4. Add the lentils, broth, thyme, sage, salt, and pepper. Bring to a simmer. Add the spinach, in batches if necessary. Cover and cook, tossing occasionally, until the spinach is wilted and the lentil mixture is thickened, about 8 to 10 minutes. Divide among 4 bowls and serve.

Note: Orange lentils, also called masoor dal, are similar to red lentils. They can be found in Asian markets and in the international section of most grocery stores. If you can't find them, substitute any lentil and cook according to package directions; green, brown, and black will hold their shape more than the orange or red. Feel free to swap in any greens for the spinach.

NUTRITION (PER SERVING):

365 calories, **26 g protein**, 39 g carbohydrates, 15 g fiber, 5 g sugars, 14 g fat, 3.5 g saturated fat, 937 mg sodium

Chicken Lettuce Tacos with Pickled Strawberry Salsa

PREP TIME: 10 minutes **TOTAL TIME:** 1 hour 5 minutes Serves 4

1 tablespoon granulated sugar

1 teaspoon kosher salt

¼ cup boiling water

½ cup cider vinegar; more as needed

2 cups halved strawberries

½ cup unsweetened coconut milk

2 garlic cloves, minced

1 pound ground chicken

½ cup chopped mint

2 teaspoons lemon zest

1 cup grape tomatoes, quartered

1 yellow bell pepper, diced

2 scallions, thinly sliced

1 jalapeno pepper, seeded and minced

8 large lettuce leaves, such as Boston

2 cups cooked brown rice

1 can (15 ounces) black beans, drained and rinsed

1. In a glass jar, stir the sugar and ½ teaspoon of the salt with the boiling water until dissolved. Add the cider vinegar and let cool to room temperature. Add the strawberries and more vinegar if needed to cover berries. Seal the lid and let stand for at least 30 minutes or up to 1 day in the refrigerator.

2. In a large skillet over medium heat, bring the coconut milk, garlic, remaining salt to a simmer. Stir in the chicken and simmer until the meat is no longer pink, stirring occasionally, about 7 minutes. Remove from the heat and stir in the mint and lemon zest.

3. Remove the strawberries from the brine and toss with the tomatoes, yellow pepper, scallions, and jalapeno.

4. Divide the chicken among the lettuce leaves and top with the strawberry salsa. Serve with the rice and beans.

Note: Using crisp lettuce as a taco base adds fresh flavor and shaves off calories. The vinegar-soaked strawberries infuses the salsa with sweet, briny taste.

NUTRITION (PER SERVING):

431 calories, **28 g protein**, 47 g carbohydrates, 9 g fiber, 8 g sugar, 16 g fat, 7 g saturated fat, 608 mg sodium

Spicy Chicken Meat Sauce and Glass Noodles

PREP TIME: 5 minutes **TOTAL TIME:** 30 minutes Serves 6

2 tablespoons olive oil

1 pound ground chicken

½ pound Italian chicken sausage, casings removed

1 yellow onion, chopped

4 cloves garlic, minced

1 teaspoon crushed red pepper flakes

1 teaspoon dried oregano

½ teaspoon kosher salt

¼ teaspoon ground black pepper

1 can (28 ounces) crushed tomatoes

1 package (about 8 ounces) glass noodles

Several leaves fresh basil, chopped

6 cups mixed green

6 tablespoons balsamic vinaigrette

1. Heat the oil in a large pot or Dutch oven over medium-high heat. Add the ground chicken and sausage. Cook, using a wooden spoon to crumble the meat thoroughly, until browned through, about 6 to 8 minutes.

2. Stir in the onion, garlic, red pepper flakes, oregano, salt, and pepper. Mix in the tomatoes, reduce the heat to medium-low, cover, and simmer, stirring occasionally, until slightly thickened, about 15 to 20 minutes.

3. Meanwhile, prepare the noodles according to package directions and drain.

4. Remove the meat sauce from the heat and serve over the prepared noodles. Sprinkle with more red pepper flakes, to taste, and the basil. Toss together the greens and the vinaigrette and serve alongside the noodles.

NUTRITION (PER SERVING):
424 calories, **23 g protein**, 49 g carbohydrates, 5 g fiber, 8 g sugars, 16 g fat, 3.5 g saturated fat, 710 mg sodium

Chipotle Chili Chicken Burgers

PREP TIME: 10 minutes **TOTAL TIME:** 25 minutes Serves 4

1½ pounds ground chicken (not ground chicken breast only)

3 canned chipotle chili peppers in adobo sauce, chopped

½ cup finely chopped white onion (about ½ medium onion)

2 cloves garlic, minced

½ teaspoon kosher salt

Canola oil, for the grill

½ cup crumbled queso fresco

4 large hearty, whole-grain buns, sliced

1 avocado, mashed

½ cup pico de gallo (or fresh salsa)

4 leaves Boston or bibb lettuce

1. Prepare a grill for medium-high heat. In a large bowl, add the chicken, peppers, onion, garlic, and salt. Use a fork to gently mix until thoroughly combined. Using wet hands, form the mixture into 4 patties, pressing an indent into the middle of each.

2. Brush the grill grates with the oil. Cook the patties on the grill, with the lid closed, until good grill marks form, about 5 minutes. Flip and top each patty with 2 tablespoons queso fresco. Close the lid and cook until the burgers reach an internal temperature of 165°F, about 5 minutes more.

3. Meanwhile, lightly toast the buns. Spread ¼ of the avocado on the inside of each top bun. Transfer the patties to the bottom buns. Top each patty with 2 tablespoons pico de gallo and 1 lettuce leaf. Close with the top bun.

Note: Look for fresh pico de gallo or any fresh salsa in the prepared foods section at the grocery store. Queso fresco is a mild fresh cheese that can be found in most grocery stores' cheese section.

NUTRITION (PER SERVING):

528 calories, **38 g protein**, 31 g carbohydrates, 6 g fiber, 8 g sugar, 29 g fat, 7.5 g saturated fat, 999 mg sodium

Asian Chicken Meatballs with Peanut Sauce

Asian Chicken Meatballs with Peanut Sauce

PREP TIME: 10 minutes **TOTAL TIME:** 30 minutes Serves 4

For the meatballs:

1 pound ground chicken

½ cup fine dry whole wheat breadcrumbs

½ cup grated onion

¼ cup grated carrot

1 large egg

1 teaspoon lime zest

1 teaspoon soy sauce

1 clove garlic, minced

½ teaspoon kosher salt

½ teaspoon ground black pepper

For the Peanut Sauce:

¼ cup natural peanut butter

2 tablespoons warm water

1 tablespoon soy sauce

1 tablespoon lime juice

1 tablespoon honey

1 teaspoon Sriracha or hot sauce

1 clove garlic, minced

1. Heat the oven to 400°F. Line a large rimmed baking sheet with parchment.

2. In a large bowl, gently mix the chicken, breadcrumbs, onion, carrot, egg, lime zest, soy sauce, garlic, salt, and pepper. Using wet hands, form into 20 rounded golf ball–size balls.

3. Place the meatballs on the prepared baking sheet, leaving 2 inches of space around each ball, and spray with cooking spray. Bake for 10 minutes, remove from the oven, and flip meatballs. Return to the oven and bake until an instant-read thermometer registers 160°F, about 5 to 10 minutes more.

4. Meanwhile, make the peanut sauce. In a small bowl, combine the peanut butter with the water, soy sauce, lime juice, honey, Sriracha, and garlic until smooth. (Makes about ½ cup.)

5. To serve, set out the meatballs with toothpicks, alongside the sauce for dipping.

Note: If you want to taste your meatballs for seasoning, take a small amount of the mix and press into a patty. Cook in a skillet with a touch of oil and taste. Adjust seasonings if needed.

NUTRITION (PER SERVING):

359 calories, **27 g protein**, 20 g carbohydrates, 3 g fiber, 8 g sugar, 19 g fat, 4 g saturated fat, 699 mg sodium

Blueberry Chicken Burgers

PREP TIME: 10 minutes **TOTAL TIME:** 30 minutes Serves 4

1 tablespoon olive oil

4 shallots, thinly sliced

2 teaspoons red wine vinegar

1 pound ground chicken

6 ounces blueberries, preferably wild

3 tablespoons plain whole wheat breadcrumbs

2 teaspoons fresh lemon juice

1 teaspoon Dijon mustard

1 clove garlic, minced

¼ teaspoon kosher salt

⅛ teaspoon ground black pepper

Canola oil for the pan

2 ounces coarsely grated Gruyere

4 multi-grain burger buns, toasted

4 small lettuce leaves

4 slices tomato

1. In a medium skillet over medium heat, heat the oil until shimmering. Add the shallots and cook, stirring, until they begin to soften and color slightly, about 8 minutes. Reduce the heat to low and cover, stirring occasionally, until the shallots become dark brown and very soft, about 10 minutes. (If the pan becomes too dry during cooking, add 1 to 2 tablespoons water). Stir in the vinegar.

2. Meanwhile, in a large bowl, combine the chicken, blueberries, breadcrumbs, lemon juice, mustard, garlic, salt, and pepper. Form into four ¾"-thick patties.

3. Heat a grill pan over medium-high until smoking. Brush oil over the grates. Grill the burgers, flipping halfway through, until grill marks form on both sides and an instant-read thermometer inserted in the center reads 165°F, about 8 minutes. Add the cheese to the burgers and cover the pan to melt, about 1 minute.

4. Place a bun on each of 4 plates. Top the bottom half with a lettuce leaf, tomato slice, burger, and the caramelized shallots and dig in.

NUTRITION (PER SERVING):

466 calories, **32 g protein**, 45 g carbohydrates, 4 g fiber, 12 g sugar, 20 g fat, 6 g saturated fat, 500 mg sodium

Chicken Meatball-Noodle Soup

PREP TIME: 20 minutes **TOTAL TIME:** 1 hour Serves 4

1 pound ground chicken

¼ teaspoon kosher salt

¼ teaspoon ground black pepper

1 tablespoon olive oil

1 yellow onion, chopped

1 cup thinly sliced carrots

6 cups low-sodium chicken broth

½ cup sliced mushrooms

½ cup thinly sliced celery

2 large kale leaves, ribs removed and leaves thinly sliced

8 ounces brown rice pasta, such as rotini, small elbows, or broken spaghetti

1. In a medium bowl, combine the chicken with the salt and pepper. Shape into 20 small balls.

2. In a Dutch oven over medium-high, heat the oil. Cook the meatballs, turning occasionally, until browned. Transfer to a plate and set aside. Add the onion and cook, stirring frequently, for 4 to 5 minutes, or until translucent. Add the carrots and cook, stirring frequently, for 1 minute. Add the broth, mushrooms, celery, and kale. Season to taste with salt and pepper. Bring to a boil, reduce the heat, and simmer until the vegetables are tender, about 15 minutes. Add the reserved meatballs to the soup and simmer until they are cooked through, about 10 to 12 minutes.

3. Meanwhile, prepare the pasta according to package directions. Drain and add to the soup. Gently stir to mix and heat through before ladling into 4 soup bowls.

NUTRITION (PER SERVING):

460 calories, **29 g protein**, 51 g carbohydrates, 3 g fiber, 3 g sugar, 13 g fat, 3 g saturated fat, 211 mg sodium